GCSE

VISUAL REVISION GUIDE

SUCCESS

DESIGN & TECHNOLOGY

RESISTANT MATERIALS

Author

Chris Hughes

CONTENTS

MATERIALS AND COMPONENTS

DESIGN AND MARKET INFLUENCES

MANUFACTURING PROCESSES

INDUSTRIAL APPLICATIONS

PROPERTIES

A property is a characteristic of a material.
A material will possess a range of different properties.
Designers use properties to help them select a material for a particular purpose.
The range of properties can be divided into mechanical, physical and aesthetic properties.
When selecting a material for a particular purpose it is necessary to consider properties for both service and manufacture.

MECHANICAL PROPERTIES

Tensile strength – ability to withstand pulling (stretching) forces.

Compressive strength – ability to withstand pushing (squashing) forces.

Shear strength – ability to withstand forces which tend to cut the material in two.

Torsional strength – ability to withstand twisting (rotary) forces.

Bending strength – ability to resist bending forces.

rope
tensile stregth
force
legs – compressive forces

bolt being sheared
force
force

motor
torsional (twisting) forces
wheel

fishing rod

Hardness – the ability of a material to withstand indentation or scratching. This is a requirement when a product or component needs to have good wear resistance. Examples include twist drills, chisels, roller bearings and kitchen cutting surfaces.

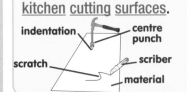
indentation
scratch
centre punch
scriber
material

Mechanical properties: these describe how a material will respond to different types of external forces.

Elasticity – a measure of how flexible a material is. Elasticity is important in products such as vaulting poles and springs.
pole
pole vaulting

Toughness – is how well a material can withstand impact forces. The opposite of toughness is brittleness. A material is said to be brittle if it has low resistance to impact loads. Toughness is important for products such as hammers, machine parts, kitchen utensils, gardening tools and railway lines.

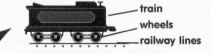
train wheels
railway lines

Machineabilty: this is how easily a material can be manufactured using machine tools.

chuck
drill
swarf

Ductility – the ability of a material to be permanently deformed by cold-working. This can be achieved by bending, twisting or pulling materials through a die. Materials for wires need to be ductile. Metals for car bodies need to be ductile so that they can be formed when pressed.

Malleability – the ability of a material to be hammered or forged into shape. The material may be shaped hot or cold.

AESTHETIC PROPERTIES

These relate to appearance:
- colour
- surface texture
- **surface decoration**
- brightness

PHYSICAL PROPERTIES

Optical properties – how well light can pass through a material. A material can be transparent, translucent or opaque.

Resistance to corrosion – how well a material will resist corrosion. **Rusting** is the main form of corrosion in steels. Most steels have to be protected against rusting.

These describe how a material will respond to physical influences other than force.

Thermal conductivity – how well a material will conduct heat. Soldering iron tips and saucepans need good thermal conductivity properties so that they can transfer heat quickly. Metals are good conductors of heat.

Electrical conductivity – how well a material conducts electricity. Electrical wires and terminals need to be good electrical conductors. Aluminium, copper and silver are examples of good conductors. **Insulators** are materials which do not conduct electricity.

PROPERTIES OF MATERIALS

SOME PROPERTIES OF COMMON MATERIALS

Mild steel	good strength properties, tough, ductile, malleable, relatively hard, poor corrosion properties	car body — good hardness properties, tough and good tensile strength
Aluminium	ductile, malleable, very good conductor of electricity and heat, good corrosion properties	ductile and malleable (so that they can be manufactured), good heat conduction, good corrosion properties, good aesthetic properties
Copper	ductile, malleable, good conductor of heat and electricity, good corrosion properties, bright appearance	plug body is a good electrical insulator, tough, relatively good overall strength properties / pins are ductile (for extrusion during manufacture), good electrical conduction, tough, wear-resistant
Beech	relatively hard, good surface appearance, tough and strong	
Spruce	relatively tough and strong, good appearance properties	
Acrylic	bright, brittle, good insulator of electricity, good optical properties, will scratch easily	
Nylon	tough, good insulator of electricity, good machineability, hard	

QUICK TEST

1. What is meant by a property of a material?
2. List the three divisions of properties.
3. Define hardness.
4. Define toughness.
5. List three properties of aluminium.
6. List three properties of acrylic.
7. What are the property requirements for the body and the pins of an electrical plug?

MATERIAL CHOICE IN DESIGN

MATERIAL SELECTION

Selecting the best material for a particular purpose is an important part of product design. Material choice depends upon its intended use and on how it will be manufactured. The environmental impact and the costs of using the material should also be considered.

PRODUCT USER NEEDS

These include the life service requirements of the product. For example, a bicycle frame needs to be rigid, strong enough to withstand the weight of the cyclist, be relatively lightweight and should not corrode during its useful life. From the needs analysis the service properties can be selected.

MANUFACTURING PROCESS

In addition to the service properties the manufacturing properties need to be considered. This is to ensure that the product can be made with the available equipment. For example, mild steel cannot be generally cast using the equipment in schools, workshops and thermosetting plastics cannot be injection-moulded. The manufacturing process must take into consideration available labour skills.

Selecting the best material depends upon the user needs of the product, the required properties and how it will be manufactured – the process.

ECONOMIC FACTORS

Material costs are an important factor in materials selection. Where possible the lowest cost alternative is selected. Costs will include the cost of buying the material and the cost of manufacture and the cost of selling.

Some manufacturing processes such as the extrusion or pressing of metals use more energy to produce the product than many plastic processing methods. This will tend to make the metal option more expensive. The manufacturing costs will depend upon the costs of preparation and finishing, the chemicals and services consumed and the size of the production area.

SERVICE PROPERTIES

Needs of bicycle frame	Service properties
Rigid	good torsional (twisting) strength and high elastic modulus
Strong	good tensile strength
Lightweight	low mass and good strength-to-weight ratio
Must not corrode	good corrosion resistance properties

MATERIAL COSTS FOR A WOODEN TOY

Cost of buying the wooden parts (purchase prices)

Cost of cutting out shapes (labour and tools)

Cost of marking out and machining (labour and tools)

Cost of finishing before paint spraying (labour and chemicals)

Cost of spraying (labour and paints)

Cost of quality checks (labour and wastage or reworking)

Cost of packaging (labour and materials)

Examiner's Top Tip
Remember to consider both service and manufacturing properties when selecting materials for a product.

MATERIAL AVAILABILITY

Materials are generally available as standard sections and parts. Metals come in: plates, strips, bars, tubes, angle irons and channels. Woods come in: dowels, sheets, planks and squares. Plastics can come in a range of forms from films and rolls to sheets and granules. Designs are often influenced by what sectional shapes are available from suppliers.

ENVIRONMENTAL CONSIDERATIONS

The following factors should influence selection:

Whether the material is a scarce resource and its use will deplete them further (e.g. using some hardwoods).

Whether the material will be harmful to the persons using it (e.g. lead-based paints).

Whether the material is disposable after use (e.g. using biodegradable materials are more environmentally friendly than non-biodegradable materials).

Whether the material can be easily recycled (e.g. steel scrap can be recycled easily).

QUICK TEST

1. State two material selection factors.
2. Why are manufacturing requirements important?
3. What factors can make up material costs?
4. State two environmental considerations when designing

MATERIAL FORMS

SHAPES AND SIZES

Materials are available in a number of standard stock sizes. Manufacturers' catalogues give the ranges available. Softwood timbers are sold in a range of machined sizes. Hardwoods tend to be sold by volume. Plastics are available in a range of forms including sheets, foams and extrusions. Metals are available in a range of different cross-sections.

TIMBER

sheets	planks	boards	strips	squares	dowels

PLASTICS

Material form		Examples of where used
films		labels, stickers and wrappers
sheet		vacuum forming or line bending
hexagonal bar		general work
square bar		general work
rods		general work
tube		general work
resins		reinforced plastics hand lay-ups
powders		injection moulding
granules		injection moulding
foams		for packaging and insulation

METALS

hexagonal bar		flat bar	
sheet		square and rectangular tube	
angle sections		round tube	
round bar		channel	
square bar		I-sections	

Steel sections come in either black mild steel or bright drawn mild steel (BDMS). Black mild steel has a black appearance and its dimensions are not too accurate. It tends to be used for forge work. Bright drawn mild steel has been drawn through dies to give an accurate finish. It can be used directly in machine vices and lathe chucks and provides a good datum surface for marking out.

Hexagonal bars and round bars can be placed directly in three jaw chucks on centre lathes.

Square bars and rectangular bars require four jaw chucks.

During the steel-making process semi-finished products include billets, blooms and slabs.
These go on to produce some of the standard stock sections by rolling or tube manufacture.

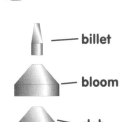

— billet

— bloom

— slab

QUICK TEST

1. **Name three forms of timber.**
2. **What is meant by the term BDMS?**
3. **How might black mild steel be used in the school workshop?**
4. **Name three types of semi-finished steel-making products.**
5. **State one use each for plastic sheet, films and granules.**

5. Vacuum forming, labels or stickers, injection moulding.
4. Billets, blooms and slabs.
3. For forge work.
2. Bright drawn mild steel.
1. From sheets, planks, boards, strips, squares or dowels.

 # METALS

TYPES OF METALS

Metals are classed as either ferrous or non-ferrous.
Ferrous metals contain iron.
Non-ferrous metals do not contain iron.
In general ferrous metals tend to corrode and therefore need some form of protection against corrosion.
Non-ferrous metals do not tend to corrode in the same way.

PURE METALS

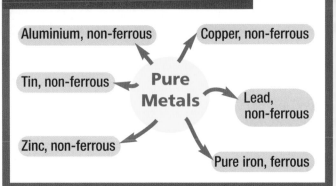

Aluminium, non-ferrous

Copper, non-ferrous

Tin, non-ferrous

Pure Metals

Lead, non-ferrous

Zinc, non-ferrous

Pure iron, ferrous

METALS AND ALLOYS

Metals are available in pure or alloy form.

Pure metals, such as pure aluminium or pure copper, contain only one type of metal. They are not mixed with any other metal.

Alloys are mixtures of two or more pure metals.

Alloys tend to have better strength properties than pure metals.

Alloys and pure metals often have special physical properties. For example, pure copper is used where electrical conductivity is required; tin and copper alloy is used for making bronze objects.

FERROUS METALS

Plain carbon steels are mixtures (alloys) of iron and carbon. The carbon content varies from about 0.01% up to about 1.5%.

Tool steels are special steels, which are alloys of iron and carbon but with other additions such as tungsten. This helps to increase their wear resistance.

The range of ferrous metals includes plain carbon steels, tool steels, stainless steels and cast irons.

Cast irons are alloys of iron and contain around 3.5–4.5% carbon. They are generally used in sand-cast products.

Stainless steels do not corrode. They are used for applications such as sinks and kitchen utensils. Stainless steels are alloys of iron and carbon but also contain chromium or nickel. These additions give it its anti-corrosive properties.

NON-FERROUS ALLOYS

Some common non-ferrous alloys:

Material	Composition	
brass	copper and zinc	
bronze	copper and tin	
duralumin	aluminium and copper	
solder	tin and lead	

PLAIN CARBON STEELS

Plain carbon steels are alloys of iron and carbon. They can be divided up into three main groups: mild steel, medium carbon steel and high carbon steel.

Mild steels have 0.15–0.35% carbon
Medium carbon steels have 0.35–0.7% carbon
High carbon steels have 0.8–1.5% carbon

Increasing the carbon content in the steel increases its hardness increases its toughness but reduces its ability to be cold-worked.

USES OF FERROUS METALS

Material	Uses	Notes
Cast iron	Vices, lathe beds, kitchen pots	Hard skin. Strong under compression. Cannot be bent or forged.
Mild steel	Nuts and bolts, screws, car bodies	Tough, ductile and malleable. Easily joined but with poor resistance to corrosion. Cannot be hardened or tempered.
High carbon steel	Tools	Very hard, but less ductile, tough and malleable. Difficult to cut. Can be hardened and tempered.
Stainless steel (alloy)	Kettles, sink surrounds, cutlery	Hard and tough. Resists wear and corrosion. Quite difficult to cut or file.
High-speed steel (alloy)	Drill bits	Very hard. Can be used as a cutting tool even when red-hot. Can only be shaped by grinding.

USES OF NON-FERROUS METALS

Material	Uses	Notes
Aluminium	Saucepans, window frames	High strength/weight ratio. Difficult to join. Good conductor of heat and electricity. Corrosion-resistant. Polishes well.
Copper	Wire, piping, circuit board	Malleable and ductile. Good conductor of heat and electricity. Easily joined. Polishes well. Expensive.
Lead	Car batteries	Very heavy, soft, malleable and ductile. Corrosion-resistant. Low melting point. Difficult to work and expensive.
Tin (tin plate)	Food cans, biscuit tins	Soft and weak. Ductile and malleable. High corrosion resistance. Low melting point. Used to coat steel to produce 'tin plate'.

QUICK TEST

1. Name two types of pure metals.
2. What two metals make up brass?
3. What two metals make up solder?
4. Name three ferrous metals.
5. What are stainless steels used for?
6. Name the three categories of plain carbon steels.
7. Give some uses for cast iron.
8. What effects does increasing the carbon content have on the properties of plain carbon steels?

1. Aluminium, tin, copper, lead, pure iron, zinc (any two)
2. Copper and zinc
3. Tin and lead
4. Stainless steel, cast iron, mild steel, tool steel, medium carbon steel, high carbon steel (any three)
5. Sinks, baths, kitchen utensils and other applications where corrosion resistance is important.
6. Mild/low carbon steel, medium carbon steel and high carbon steel.
7. Vices, lathe beds, some kitchen pots, car cylinder blocks.
8. It increases hardness, increases toughness and decreases the ability to be cold-worked.

HEAT TREATMENT PROCESSES

CHANGING THE PROPERTIES OF METALS

The properties of some metals can be altered by heat treatments.
Heat treatment processes may be used to improve the properties of the metal.
They are also used to help soften the metal for use in processes such as cold rolling, cold extrusion and wire drawing of metals.
During heat treatment the metal is heated and cooled in a controlled way to give the required properties.

HEAT TREATMENT

The main heat treatment processes are:
The annealing of non-ferrous and ferrous metals to make them less brittle.
The normalising of medium carbon steels to make them more stable.
The hardening and tempering of steels above 0.4% carbon content to improve toughness on impact.
The case-hardening of mild steels to improve strength.

HARDENING AND TEMPERING

HARDENING AND TEMPERING
Hardening and tempering of steels can only be used for steels that have a carbon content greater that about 0.4%. Steels that have less than this amount can however be case-hardened.
Hardening and tempering is used to increase the hardness of products such as chisels, hammers, scribers, centre punches and hacksaw blades. The process is also used to give springs their 'springiness'. Components are first hardened and then tempered. Tempering reduces the brittleness that results from the hardening process. Products are therefore more reliable in service.

WORK HARDENING

When a metal is hammered, rolled, squeezed or pulled through a die it will tend to become harder. As the metal hardens it becomes more difficult to work with. It will eventually become so hard that no more work can be carried out without it cracking or breaking. Annealing softens the metal so that further cold work can be carried out. Annealing can be carried out in the school workshop using a brazing torch. In industry it tends to be carried out using furnaces at the required annealing temperature.

FORGING AND ROLLING

Annealing will change the distorted grains back to their original shape. In doing so it will re-soften the metal and further cold work can be carried out.

When a cold metal is squeezed during forging or rolling its internal grain structure distorts. The greater the distortion the more the metal will work-harden.

press

die

die

product may require annealing for further shaping

rollers

grains heavily distorted after rolling

ANNEALING

Annealing *is a heat treatment process which is used to soften a metal once it has become work-hardened. Annealing can also be used to reduce internal stresses which occur during cold work.*

ANNEALING TEMPERATURES

Annealing temperatures for some common metals are given in the table.
The temperatures show furnace settings for the correct treatment. The colours give an approximate indication of the temperatures reached when using a brazing torch in the school workshop.

TYPE OF METAL	ANNEALING FURNACE SETTINGS (°C)	COLOURS FOR USE WITH BRAZING TORCH	HOW COOLED
Non-ferrous metals			
Copper	500	Heat to a dull red	In air
Brass	560	Heat to a dull red	In air
Aluminium	370–410	Cover the metal with soap. When the soap turns black the correct annealing temperature has been reached	Leave to cool slowly
Ferrous metals			
Steel	730	Heat to a cherry red	Cool slowly in a furnace

NORMALISING

Normalising is an industrial process used to improve the strength and toughness of products when they have been forged or rolled. Normalising improves the internal structure of the metal and reduces the internal stresses that have been produced by hot working. The temperature at which the steel is heated depends upon the carbon content of the steel. After heating the steel is cooled in air.

QUICK TEST

1. What is meant by the term 'heat treatment'?
2. Name four heat treatment processes
3. What is meant by 'annealing'?
4. What materials are normalised?
5. How can household soap be used to indicate the correct annealing temperature of aluminium?
6. What do the colours indicate when tempering with a brazing torch?
7. Which metal is usually hardened by case hardening?

1. Heating and cooling a metal in a controlled way to alter its properties.
2. Annealing, normalising, hardening and tempering and case-hardening.
3. To soften a metal after it has work hardened.
4. Steels.
5. When it turns a black.
6. The temperature the metal is at.
7. Mild steel.

13

PLASTICS

Plastic materials can be classed as either thermoplastics or thermosetting plastics. Thermoplastics have the ability to return to their original shape when reheated. This is termed plastic memory. Thermosets cannot be reformed when reheated. Thermoplastics can be recycled in manufacturing processes such as injection moulding. Thermosetting plastics cannot be recycled in this way. Thermosetting plastics can generally withstand higher operating temperatures than thermoplastics.

THE STRUCTURE OF PLASTICS

Plastic materials are made up of many long chain molecules called polymers. These consist of a 'backbone' of carbon atoms with other types of atoms attached to it. These may be hydrogen, oxygen, chlorine or nitrogen atoms. Different types of plastics have different arrangements of atoms attached to the main backbone. A plastics material will have many thousands of individual polymer chains which are held together by the atomic forces between the chains.

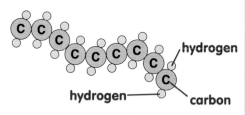

atomic structure of polythene

THERMOPLASTICS

When a thermoplastic is heated and reshaped the atomic bonds between the molecules are weakened. The molecules can then slide, move and re-align themselves into new positions. If the plastic is re-heated the bonds can be weakened again. This will allow further re-shaping or a return to its original shape.

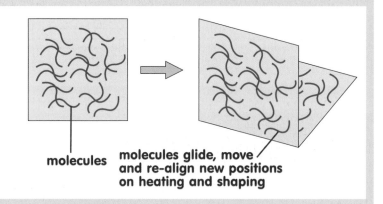

molecules

molecules glide, move and re-align new positions on heating and shaping

THERMOSETTING PLASTICS

In order for thermosetting plastics to be formed they need to go through a curing stage. During curing molecular links are formed between the original long chain molecules. This is termed cross-linking. Cross-linking is irreversible and so thermosetting plastics cannot be re-formed once curing has taken place. Because of cross-linking thermosetting plastics tend to be more rigid than thermoplastics. They can also withstand higher operating temperatures.

Because thermosets need to have a curing stage during moulding they are manufactured by compression moulding or transfer moulding.

PRODUCTION PROCESSES FOR THERMOPLASTICS

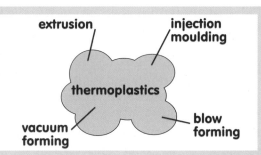

extrusion

injection moulding

thermoplastics

vacuum forming

blow forming

COMMON PLASTICS

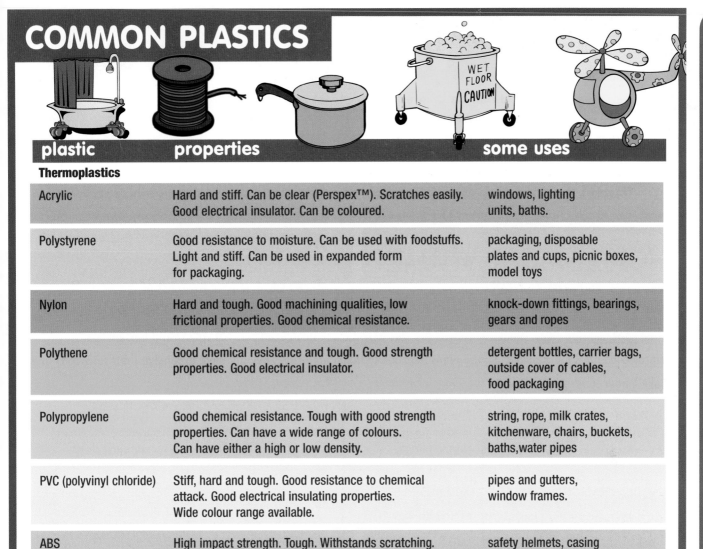

plastic	properties	some uses
Thermoplastics		
Acrylic	Hard and stiff. Can be clear (Perspex™). Scratches easily. Good electrical insulator. Can be coloured.	windows, lighting units, baths.
Polystyrene	Good resistance to moisture. Can be used with foodstuffs. Light and stiff. Can be used in expanded form for packaging.	packaging, disposable plates and cups, picnic boxes, model toys
Nylon	Hard and tough. Good machining qualities, low frictional properties. Good chemical resistance.	knock-down fittings, bearings, gears and ropes
Polythene	Good chemical resistance and tough. Good strength properties. Good electrical insulator.	detergent bottles, carrier bags, outside cover of cables, food packaging
Polypropylene	Good chemical resistance. Tough with good strength properties. Can have a wide range of colours. Can have either a high or low density.	string, rope, milk crates, kitchenware, chairs, buckets, baths, water pipes
PVC (polyvinyl chloride)	Stiff, hard and tough. Good resistance to chemical attack. Good electrical insulating properties. Wide colour range available.	pipes and gutters, window frames.
ABS	High impact strength. Tough. Withstands scratching. Resistant to chemicals.	safety helmets, casing for household goods, car parts
PTFE	Low frictional properties. Tough. Good chemical resistance Used for bearing surfaces	surface for non-stick pans, plumbers' tape,
Thermosetting plastics		
Polyester resin	Hard, strong and brittle. Good electrical and heat insulating properties.	used with reinforced plastics for boat hulls and chemical vessels
Urea-formaldehyde	Hard, stiff and brittle. Good electrical and heat-resistant properties.	electrical fittings, electrical switches
Melamine formaldehyde	Hard, stiff. Resists scratching. Good heat-resistant properties. Stain-resistant. Good range of colours available	work surfaces, kitchenware.

QUICK TEST

1. What is meant by thermoplastic material?
2. Name two types of thermosetting plastics materials.
3. Name two types of thermoplastics materials.
4. What happens to a thermosetting plastic when it is cured?
5. State two production processes used to form thermoplastics.
6. Name a production process used to form a thermosetting plastics.
7. Give a use for polystyrene.
8. Give a use for PVC.
9. State two advantages of using plastics.

9. Can be coloured, does not corrode, resistant to chemical attack, good electrical insulator, can be formed at low operating temperatures.
8. Pipes and gutters and window frames.
7. Packaging, disposable plates and cups, picnic boxes and model toys.
6. Compression moulding or transfer moulding.
5. Injection moulding, blow moulding, vacuum forming or extrusion.
4. Molecular cross-links are formed.
3. Nylon, acrylic, polystyrene, polythene, polypropylene, PVC, ABS or PTFE.
2. From polyester resin, urea-formaldehyde or melamine formaldehyde.
1. A plastic that can return to its original shape when re-heated.

WOODS

Wood can be divided into natural and man-made timbers.
Natural timbers are further sub-divided into hardwoods and softwoods. Man-made timbers include plywood, MDF and blockboards. Hardwoods come from broad leaf trees, many of which shed their leaves in autumn. Softwoods come from coniferous trees.
All timbers require protection against rotting and fungal disease.

HARDWOODS AND THEIR USES

The terms 'hardwood' and 'softwood' are not physical classifications which refer to hardness of the wood. They are biological classifications. Hardwoods come from trees which carry their seeds in the form of fruit. Softwoods come from cone-bearing trees. Some hardwoods are soft to work. Common examples are willow and balsa wood. Hardwoods are slow-growing, taking many decades to reach maturity. They are more expensive than softwoods and take longer to re-grow.

Wood		Typical uses	Wood		Typical uses
Mahogany		indoor furniture, shop fittings, veneers	Teak		quality furniture, veneers, boat building
Beech		chairs, workbenches, tools	Jelutong		patterns for moulds, product models
Ash		tool handles, hockey sticks, ladders	Balsa		modelling
Oak		garden furniture, high-quality indoor furniture, boat hulls	Willow		sports equipment, outdoor wicker work

SOFTWOODS AND THEIR USES

Softwoods come from coniferous trees, which reach maturity in around 30 years. This allows them to be replaced at a far faster rate than hardwoods. This is better for the environment and also reduces the cost. Softwoods tend to be used much more than hardwoods.

Examiner's Top Tip
Learn some uses for common hardwoods and softwoods.

Wood		Typical uses	Wood		Typical uses
Scots pine		constructional work and joinery	Western red cedar		wall panels, out door furniture, sheds and fences
Spruce		general indoor work, furniture	Parana pine		good quality joinery, staircases and built-in furniture

TIMBER

Dry rot is a fungus that can occur in damp, unventilated situations. The wood becomes dry and powdery.

dampness

Wet rot is caused by wet and damp conditions. The timber becomes weak and spongy.

Wood needs protecting against **insect attack** such as woodworm and lyctus beetle.

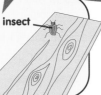
insect

Timber is prone to **defects** which can cause some difficulties when it is being worked. If left unprotected insect and fungal attack can weaken the strength of the wood.

Splits will weaken the structure of the timber. They can spoil the appearance of the wood. slits

Wood may **shrink** even after it has been **seasoned**.

Knots weaken the wood and can cause problems when using hand and machine tools.

knots

MANUFACTURED BOARDS

Advantages of using man-made boards

- Available in large sheets of uniform thickness.
- Not affected by humidity.
- Can be used with veneers.
- Do not have a grain structure.
- More easily worked than natural timbers.
- Can be easily joined with knock-down fittings.

veneer

plywood — layers

chipboard

medium density fibreboard (MDF) — smooth

blockboard

hardboard — smooth, rough

QUICK TEST

1. What are the two main divisions of timber products?
2. Name two types of hardwoods.
3. Name two types of softwoods.
4. What classification is balsa wood?
5. State a use for ash.
6. State a use for Scots pine.
7. Name two defects that may be found in timbers.
8. State two advantages of using man-made boards.

1. Natural and man-made.
2. Mahogany, beech, ash, oak, teak, jelutong or willow.
3. Scots pine, spruce, western red cedar or Parana pine.
4. Hardwood.
5. Tool handles, hockey sticks or ladders.
6. Constructional work and joinery.
7. Shrinkage, knots, splits, dry rot, wet rot or insect attack.
8. Available in large sheets, can be veneered, do not have a grain structure, easily joined, not affected by humidity.

COMPOSITE MATERIALS AND SMART MATERIALS

MODERN REPLACEMENT MATERIALS

Composites are now being widely used as replacements for metals and plastics.
Two of the main types are fibre-reinforced composites and sandwich beam constructions.
Fibre-based composites consist of strong fibres such as glass, carbon or kevlar embedded in a metal or plastics matrix.
Sandwich beam constructions consist of a lightweight core material sandwiched between thin-skin materials.
Smart materials are materials whose properties can change due to changes in pressure, force or temperature.

FIBRE-BASED COMPOSITES

laminate

laminae

Fibre-based composites are made up of layers of fibre embedded in a matrix material. Each layer is called a lamina (plural laminae) and a number of layers make up a laminate. Common fibres are glass fibres (fibre glass), carbon fibres and kevlar. They all have good tensile properties and their use in the composite improves the stiffness and strength of the material.
The matrix material can be either a thermoplastic or thermosetting plastic or a metal such as aluminium or titanium.

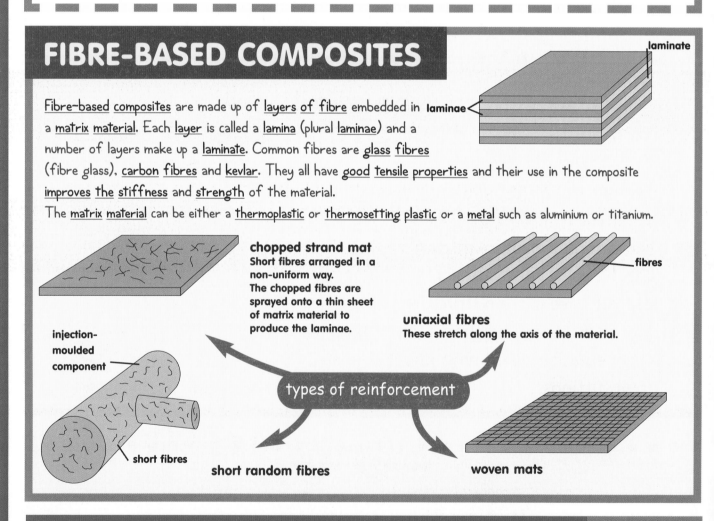

chopped strand mat
Short fibres arranged in a
non-uniform way.
The chopped fibres are
sprayed onto a thin sheet
of matrix material to
produce the laminae.

fibres

uniaxial fibres
These stretch along the axis of the material.

injection-moulded component

short fibres

types of reinforcement

short random fibres

woven mats

USES OF FIBRE-BASED COMPOSITES

Sports equipment
Chemical vessels and pipework
Transport applications
Boat hulls
Bullet-proof vests
Crash helmets
Aircraft parts

SANDWICH CONSTRUCTIONS

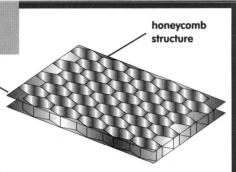

Sandwich <u>constructions</u> are used in many <u>transport applications</u>. A common type is a lightweight <u>core material</u> such as paper or aluminium honeycomb sandwiched between two <u>tough outer skins</u>. The skins are bonded to the core material by a strong adhesive. This construction is used in many aircraft structures and in house doors. These structures are lightweight as well as being strong.

SOME METHODS OF FIBRE COMPOSITE MANUFACTURE

<u>Pultrusion</u> where constant cross sections of fibre and matrix can be pulled through dies.

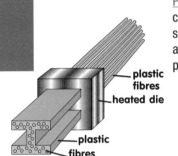

<u>Hand lay-up</u> where alternative composite layers are moulded onto a former. This method can be used in school workshops.

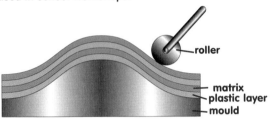

<u>Filament winding</u> where products such as pipes and chemical vessels are produced automatically on a filament-winding machine.

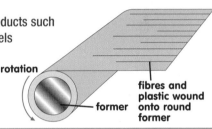

SMART MATERIALS

<u>Smart materials</u> have properties which can <u>alter</u> in response to an <u>input</u>. They are mainly used for <u>sensors</u>.
The main types are <u>piezoelectric sensors</u> and <u>shape memory alloys</u>.
<u>Piezoelectric sensors</u> produce an <u>output voltage</u> when <u>squeezed</u>. Typical uses are burglar alarm pressure sensors.
<u>Shape memory alloys</u> are able to change their <u>shape</u> in response to <u>changes in temperature</u>. One application is in <u>glasshouse window openers</u>. Here the material responds to changes in temperature and is as part of the ventilation mechanism.

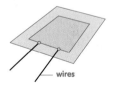
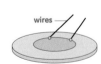

examples of piezo actuators

QUICK TEST

1. Name two types of composite materials.
2. Name two types of smart materials.
3. Give two uses of fibre-based composites.
4. Give a use for smart materials.
5. State two methods of manufacturing composites.
6. Give two advantages of using composite materials.

1. Fibre composite and sandwich beam.
2. Piezoelectric and shape-memory alloys.
3. Sports equipment, pipework, transport applications, boat hulls, bullet-proof vests, crash helmets or aircraft parts.
4. Burglar alarm sensors and parts of greenhouse window openers.
5. Hand lay-up, pultrusion and filament winding.
6. Light weight, good strength-to-weight ratio, good corrosion resistance, easily manufactured.

COMPONENTS AND ADHESIVES

Standard components such as nuts, bolts, set screws and washers are used in the assembly of products and systems. They also include gears, pulleys and bearings. Standard components are usually bought in from suppliers. Buying in standard components tends to be a cheaper option than manufacturing them individually. Most standard components are classified as temporary fixings. These can be taken apart if required. Adhesives form permanent joints. Adhesives can be used to bond metals, plastics or wood materials.

TEMPORARY FIXINGS

bolts

Bolts tend to made from mild steel. High tensile steels are used for higher strength applications. The thread of a bolt does not go all the way to its head.

coach bolt

Coach bolts are used for attaching metal parts to wood. They have a domed head with a square underneath. The square embeds in the wood and acts as a locking device.

set screws

Set screws have threads that go the whole way along its length. They tend to be used where an accurate assembly of parts is required.

spring washer   **tab washer**

Washers protect the surfaces from damage when nuts are tightened up. Spring washers and tab washers may be used to make the nuts more secure.

self-tapping screw

Self-tapping screws are made from hardened steel. They cut their own thread when they are screwed in to pre-drilled metal. They are generally used for joining together sheet metal parts.

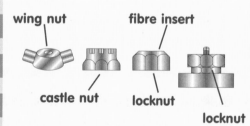

wing nut   **fibre insert**

castle nut   **locknut**

locknut

There are many types of nuts which can be used with set screws and bolts.
Castle nuts are used with a split pin to lock it place. *Locknuts* have nylon inserts to prevent them from working loose due to vibrations. *Thin lock nuts* can be used with a standard nut to prevent it from working loose.

TAPPING DRILL SIZES

When internal threads are produced using taps the holes are drilled using an appropriate tapping drill size.

Clearance holes are used to ensure that the bolts and set screws fit through holes without interference.

thread size (mm)	tapping drill size (mm)	thread size (mm)	tapping drill size (mm)
3	2.5	10	8.5
4	3.3	12	10.2
5	4.2	14	12.0
6	5.0	16	14.0
8	6.8		

PERMANENT FIXINGS

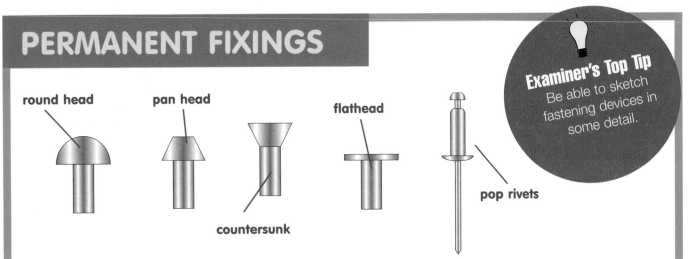

round head   pan head   flathead

countersunk

pop rivets

Examiner's Top Tip
Be able to sketch fastening devices in some detail.

Rivets are one type of standard component which gives a permanent fixing. They can be used to join metals or plastics together. Standard rivets can have a round head, flat head, pan head or be countersunk. Pop rivets are used to join sheet materials together.

ADHESIVES

Adhesives can either be natural or synthetic. Synthetic types tend to be toxic and have to be handled with care. Contact adhesives are used for large surface areas.

Adhesive	Use
Polyvinyl acetate (PVA)	White wood glue. Easy to use. Not waterproof.
Synthetic resin (Cascamite)	Used to glue wood. Stronger than PVA. Supplied as powder and mixed with water. Good waterproof properties.
Epoxy resin (Araldite)	Can be used on metals, wood and plastics. It is a two-part glue which needs to be mixed together.
Acrylic cement (Tensol)	Used to bond together certain plastics.

Good adhesive joints depend upon:
- Ensuring that the gluing surfaces are clean and free from dirt and moisture.
- Using the correct adhesive for the job.
- Using clamps to apply pressure to the joints.
- Cleaning the excess adhesive from the joints prior to setting.

QUICK TEST

1. Name three types of standard components.
2. Name the type of bolt used for attaching metal parts to wood.
3. Name two types of nuts.
4. What are spring washers used for?
5. Name two types of rivet head.
6. What is Tensol cement used for?

6. Bonding certain plastics.
5. Round head, flat head, pan head or countersunk.
4. To stop nut and bolt working loose if vibrated.
3. Wing nut, locknut or castle nut.
2. Coach bolt.
1. Nuts, bolts, set screws, washers, self-tapping screws, bearings and gears.

EXAM QUESTIONS – Use the questions to test your progress. Check your answers on page 94.

1. A letter rack is to be made from 5 mm thick plastic.

a) Name a plastic suitable for making the rack. (1 mark)

....

b) State one reason why you have chosen the material. (1 mark)

....

5mm plastics

2. a) Name a wood commonly used in the manufacture of children s toys. (1 mark)

....

b) State two reasons why people may prefer plastic toys to wooden toys. (2 marks)

....

3. a) Name three ready-made components that can be bought from suppliers. (3 marks)

....

b) State two reasons why these components are often bought in from such companies. (2 marks)

....

4. A wooden toy needs to be sent through the post.

a) Give two suitable packaging materials you could use and give one reason for each choice. (2 marks)

....

b) State one environmental issue associated with each material you have chosen. (1 mark)

....

5. A set of direction arrows for outside use are to be made from mild steel.

a) State two properties the direction arrows would have to have. (2 marks)

....

b) Give a reason why unprotected mild steel is not suitable for outdoor use. (1 mark)

....

c) Explain how mild steel could be protected. (1 mark)

....

6. a) Give two reasons why manufactured boards are better for the environment than natural timbers. (2 marks)

....

b) Name two types of manufactured boards. (2 marks)

....

7. A softwood box is to made in batches of 9000.

a) Name a material to make (i) the box and (ii) the thermoplastic handle. (2 marks)

....

b) Give one property associated with each of the materials you have named. (1 mark)

....

c) State a process that could be used to manufacture the handles. (1 mark)

....

8. A batch of screwdriver blades are to be quench-hardened and tempered.

a) What type of steel would be suitable? (1 mark)

....

b) Why does the metal need tempering? (1 mark)

....

c) How can the correct tempering temperature be identified? (1 mark)

....

9. Twenty canoe hulls are to be made from a composite material.

a) State what sort of composite could be used. (1 mark)

....

b) Give two advantages of using the composite material as opposed to other types of materials. (2 marks)

....

c) What process could be used to manufacture the hull? (1 mark)

....

10. a) Name a natural wood suitable for outside use. (1 mark)

....

b) Give two reasons why it needs to be protected. (2 marks)

....

11. Two parts of an acrylic picture stand are to be glued together.

a) Name a type of adhesive that could be used. (1 mark)

....

b) State two factors that need to be observed to ensure a good joint. (2 marks)

....

12. A material is being selected for a washing-up bowl. (2 marks)

a) List two required properties for the bowl.

....

b) Name a suitable material for the bowl. (1 mark)

....

c) Name an alternative metal that could be used. (1 mark)

....

How did you do?

1–3	correct	start again
4–6	correct	getting there
7–9	correct	good work
10–12	correct	excellent

PRODUCT ANALYSIS

Product analysis is where existing products are studied to gather information about their purpose, design and methods of manufacture. Product analysis is useful in resistant materials technology for the following reasons:

It can help to **generate** **additional** **ideas**.

It provides **case** **study** **examples** of good or bad industrial design and manufacture.

It can identify why a product is successful and what important decisions have been made during the **design** **and** **development** stages.

DESIGN IDEAS

Designs are rarely totally new. Most designs are adaptations, modifications and updates of existing products. Changes to a product might include using new materials, having a different style, making it more efficient and keeping in line with new safety standards.

It is, therefore, useful to study a range of existing products in the initial stages of project work.

PRODUCT ANALYSIS CHECKLIST

When carrying out an analysis use a checklist to help identify the important elements. These can include:

- a description of the product
- its purpose
- its working principles
- aesthetic, ergonomic and safety features
- manufacturing routes and costs
- environmental issues.

Where possible, disassemble the product to gain an understanding of how it works and how the parts fit together. Sketch or photograph parts for future reference. It is worthwhile paying particular attention to how parts fit together. Look for clips on plastics casings, how screws and fasteners are held in place and how components such as batteries and motors fit into the main body. Taking the product apart can help determine which materials and manufacturing processes have been used.

SUITABLE PRODUCTS

There are many products that can be used for an analysis.

Electric kettles, garden tools, lamps, cameras, watches, bicycles, portable tools, sewing machines, food packaging, hairdryers, children's toys, playgroup equipment, personal stereos.

INDUSTRIAL AND MANUFACTURING PROCESSES

Most products will be made in <u>industry</u>. They will, generally, be made in <u>batches</u> or in large <u>continuous</u> <u>quantities</u>. Factors to consider in an analysis might be <u>how many</u> components are made, why this number is made in relation to the <u>market</u>, what types of <u>production systems</u> are used in the manufacture and how the products are <u>packaged</u> and <u>marketed</u>.

Materials
What materials are used?
Reasons for their choice.
Details of finishing.

Assembly
Description of the fixings that are used.
How parts locate in place.
How can the product be taken apart for maintenance and changing parts.

Manufacturing
What are the main production routes?
Reasons for choosing the routes.
Details of quantities manufactured/sold.

What to include in an analysis

Environmental issues
Can parts of the product be recycled?
Are any parts made from biodegradable materials?
Is the product safe to use?
Are any environmentally unfriendly processes used in its production?

Working principles
Does the project incorporate any mechanisms?
If so, how does it work?
How are the mechanisms maintained?
How reliable is the product?

Aesthetics and ergonomics

Background to the product
The name and type of product.
A description of its intended use.
How the product works and how it is used.
Photographs, sketches, diagrams of product.
Short description of the parts and how it is assembled.
Exploded views of the parts.

www.design-process.co.uk

QUICK TEST

1. How can product analysis aid design and technology?
2. What factors can be studied during an analysis?
3. What types of products make suitable case studies?
4. What materials factors would you look for in an analysis?

GENERATING DESIGN PROPOSALS

Generating a design proposal is the first stage of a design and technology project.
Generating a proposal is made easier by having a sequence of activities to work through.
Design proposals start from having a project need.
In industry there are a number of inventive ways in which a design need may occur.
In schools a project need is best generated from a range of real situations.

Examiner's Top Tip
Remember to consider both manufacturing process and product specifications.

INDUSTRIAL PROJECTS

The are a <u>number</u> <u>of</u> <u>reasons</u> why design projects are generated in industry.
Many companies need to <u>continually</u> <u>generate</u> <u>design</u> <u>ideas</u> so that the company is able to <u>keep</u> <u>in</u> <u>business</u>. For example, the continuous updating of <u>mobile</u> <u>phones</u>, <u>computers</u>, <u>kitchen</u> <u>products</u> and <u>computer</u> <u>games</u> <u>consoles</u>.
There may be <u>fashion</u> <u>changes</u> which create <u>design</u> <u>opportunities</u>. These are a response to changes in <u>people's</u> <u>tastes</u>.
Companies often use <u>planned</u> <u>obsolescence</u> to make products <u>outdated</u> or <u>break</u> <u>down</u> after a certain number of years.
A <u>new</u> <u>technology</u> can be a stimulus to new forms of design. For example, the invention of the silicon microchip has allowed many thousands of products to be designed and manufactured over the last 30 years.
<u>Design</u> <u>opportunities</u> can also arise through <u>improvement</u> of <u>existing</u> <u>products</u>.
This might include using better materials, <u>safety</u> <u>features</u>, making the product more <u>environmentally</u> <u>friendly</u> and making the product more <u>energy-efficient</u>.
A <u>design</u> <u>need</u> can therefore be for a large number of reasons.

INTERNET
www.designtechnology.org

SCHOOL PROJECTS

School projects are best generated from <u>real</u> <u>situations</u>.
Real situations can come from a wide range of areas or contexts. Here are a few:
- Garden centres, playgroups, the home, schools, youth clubs, leisure activities, leisure centres, old people's homes and small businesses.
- Projects are often based around one of these situations.
<u>Research</u> can be carried out to <u>find</u> <u>a</u> <u>specific</u> <u>need</u> for a project.
Choosing an area and finding a need will be the <u>starting</u> <u>point</u> for the project.

STAGES IN GENERATING A PROPOSAL

- Choose an area of study (context) from which a project need can be found.
- Define the project need – purpose of the project.
- Prepare a design brief.
- Write the specification for the project.
- Carry out research to help in the initial design stages.
- Use graphics, annotated notes, diagrams, photographs, tape recordings and other methods to generate initial design ideas.
- Use cardboard and other suitable materials to make models to test early designs.
- Select the best idea or ideas for further development. Give reasons for choices and rejection.

DESIGN BRIEF

This is a <u>statement</u> of the <u>problem</u> <u>to</u> <u>be</u> <u>solved</u>. In industry it is the <u>set</u> <u>of</u> <u>instructions</u> that are passed on to the designer. In the school situation the design brief is a written statement outlining the <u>design</u> <u>problem</u>.

A design brief should include a <u>product</u> <u>specification</u> which gives specific details about the product. <u>Specifications</u> usually include information about how a product should perform. These can be factors such as:

- temperature ranges
- weight of the product
- maximum dimensions of a product
- speed of rotation
- target cost
- safety specifications.

PRODUCT SPECIFICATION DETAILS

Other less measurable factors that can be included in a specification include:

- how the product will be used
- colour
- size and shape
- ergonomic factors
- reliability factors
- maintenance requirements
- the manufacturing specifications.

THE MANUFACTURING PROCESS

This will influence the design. Factors might include:

- the quantity of products to be made
- which machines are available
- the quality specifications for the product
- the timescale for manufacture
- the cost (budget) limitations.

RESEARCH

Plan research carefully. Make sure that you:

- know what you want to find out
- where to get information
- who to talk to
- evaluate products on the market
- research the needs of the product
- use the design specification to plan research.

QUICK TEST

1. What is a design brief?
2. What is a product specification?
3. What might be included in a manufacturing specification?
4. What are the stages in generating a design proposal?

1. A statement of the problem to be solved.
2. Gives specific details about a design project.
3. Quantity of products made, machines available, quality factors, timescale.
4. Design brief, detailing the specifications, proposed manufacturing route, research.

PRODUCT DEVELOPMENT AND PLANNING

During **product development**, work is carried out to transform the **initial** design **proposal** into **working drawings** ready for manufacture.
Development makes use of **sketches**, **further research** and **mock-ups** to refine ideas.
Planning is essential to plan the **manufacturing route**, the **manufacturing times** and how **quality** and other factors will be **controlled**.
Computer-aided drawing is widely used to produce the **final working drawings**.

DEVELOPMENT

It is important to develop an idea into a practical solution. This involves:

- further drawing of how parts fit together
- selecting the materials
- making mock-ups
- using mock-ups to test ideas
- gathering information from people or groups
- producing development
- sketches and working drawings.

MOCK-UPS

Mock-ups can be used so that accurate measurements can be worked out. They can also help with aesthetic and ergonomic decisions. Mock-ups are quicker and cheaper to produce than the final products and can help reduce problems during manufacturing. Mock-ups are used for many applications in industry from clay models of cars through to models of kitchen equipment. These help designers to visualise the product in its three-dimensional form. Computer modelling has replaced the need for hard modelling in many instances.

WORKING DRAWINGS

From sketches and models working drawings can be made. These are drawings of the components ready for manufacture.
Computer-aided design (CAD) is used to produce working drawings.
The purpose of working drawings is to ensure that all the information to make the product is given. This includes the dimensions of the product, the surface finishes required and the types of materials used. Where tolerances are required these are added.
A cutting list is required so that production can be planned.

CHECK LIST

Design development should:

- clearly show how the final product will function
- consider the aesthetic and style details
- finalise cost and price
- consider the ergonomic principles
- finalise materials
- consider the health and safety issues
- consider the environmental issues
- design for easy assembly at the manufacturing stage.

PLANNING

Most <u>planning</u> will be for <u>batch</u> <u>manufacture</u>. <u>Standardised</u> <u>parts</u> can be used to <u>simplify</u> the production route and <u>reduce</u> <u>costs</u>.

Planning includes:

- planning the stages of manufacture to fit the time available
- deciding the best sequence for the operations to be carried out
- planning to have materials ready in time for the operations.

PLANNING CHARTS

<u>Gantt</u> <u>charts</u> and <u>network</u> <u>charts</u> are used to help plan and record production.

A <u>Gantt</u> <u>chart</u> is a <u>graph</u> which shows the <u>project</u> <u>stages</u> on a <u>timescale</u>. Gantt charts are used widely for <u>managing</u> <u>projects</u>. The charts give a visual plan of the project stages. Gantt charts can be used to check whether the stages of the project are being carried out on time. If not, measures can be taken to speed the process up.

<u>Network</u> <u>charts</u> are <u>activity</u> <u>charts</u> which can be used to show the <u>route</u> through a <u>manufacturing</u> <u>system</u>. The arrows on the chart indicate the <u>flow</u> <u>of</u> <u>materials</u> and show the order in which the work will be carried out.

Gantt Chart

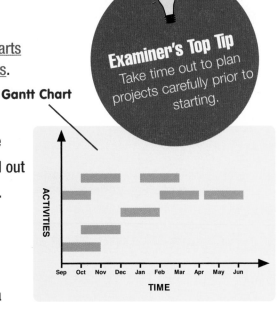

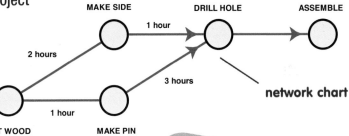

network chart

INTERNET
www.tep.org.uk

AESTHETICS

This is concerned with the <u>appearance</u> of the product. It is concerned with aspects such as the colour and texture of the product, the style, shape and proportions.

ERGONOMICS

<u>Ergonomic</u> <u>factors</u> relate the product to the user. This might include ensuring that dimensions are appropriate for the user's height or size of hands, switches can be seen and that the product is not too heavy. <u>Anthropometric</u> <u>data</u> can be used for the ergonomic aspects of a design.

QUICK TEST

1. **What types of activities are carried out during product development?**
2. **What is meant by aesthetics?**
3. **Why are working drawings needed?**
4. **What type of charts can be used for planning?**

1. Sketches, further research, making mock-ups, further drawings of how parts fit together.
2. The appearance of the product – style, colour, texture, shape and proportions.
3. To ensure that all the information to make the product is given.
4. Gantt and network charts.

SOCIAL AND ENVIRONMENTAL CARE

It is important to <u>design</u> <u>products</u> so that they are <u>socially</u> <u>acceptable</u> and do not have any adverse effects on <u>the</u> <u>environment</u>. <u>Technology</u> should be <u>used</u> in a <u>responsible</u> <u>way</u>.

RECYCLED MATERIALS

Many materials can be <u>recycled</u> in one form or another. This helps the total stock of a material from becoming <u>scarce</u>. Examples of recycled materials include <u>card</u> and <u>paper</u>, <u>metals</u> and <u>thermoplastics</u>. <u>Manufactured</u> <u>boards</u> are made from <u>reconstituted</u> <u>and</u> <u>recycled</u> <u>timber</u> reducing the use or over-use of trees.

CHECK LIST

The following items should be considered:

What impact will the product have on the environment?

Can use be made of recycled resources?

Can non-renewable resources be reduced?

Can waste be reused?

Can biodegradable products be used?

Is the design energy efficient?

Are there any toxic waste products?

Are there any harmful components in the design?

Is the product safe, user-friendly and unlikely to be misused?

IMPACT ON THE ENVIRONMENT

There are many ways in which a design can have an <u>impact</u> on the <u>environment</u>. For example, a product may use up <u>scarce</u> <u>resources</u>, its production process may produce <u>harmful</u> <u>wastes</u> or the product may contain <u>toxic</u> <u>substances</u>.
Designers need to be aware of <u>environmental</u> <u>problems</u> and develop designs which are <u>environmentally</u> <u>friendly</u>. There are now a number of national and <u>international</u> <u>regulations</u> that govern environmental issues.

RENEWABLE AND NON-RENEWABLE RESOURCES

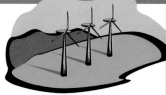

A <u>renewable</u> <u>resource</u> is one which can be renewed in a relatively short time period. Examples are <u>timbers</u> and materials from plants and animals. <u>Wind</u>, <u>water</u> and <u>solar</u> <u>power</u> are examples of <u>renewable</u> <u>energy</u> <u>sources</u>.
Softwoods grow quicker than hardwoods and renew at a faster rate.
<u>Metals</u> are <u>non-renewable</u>. Their ores have taken many years to form. They will not be formed in the same way again. As the supply of the metal is used up the stock will eventually disappear. In a similar way plastics are made from oil which is again non-renewable.

REDUCING WASTE AND ENERGY

Waste can be reduced by selecting and using materials wisely. When using sheet materials make sure that they are marked out to produce minimum waste. Templates can be arranged on top of the sheet in the most efficient way. When machining use the nearest size stock bars to reduce the levels of wasted materials. Standard components can help reduce the need to use specially made components. Processes that use plastics, often, require less energy than making parts out of metals. This helps reduce the amount of wasted energy in the form of heat and electricity.

BIODEGRADABLE MATERIALS

These are <u>better</u> for the <u>environment</u> than ones that may take many years to <u>decompose</u>. Parts of a design can be made from biodegradable materials so that they can be <u>disposed of easily</u>. This is an important factor in the design of <u>packaging</u> where the materials are thrown away without any further use.

TOXIC PRODUCTS AND HARMFUL COMPONENTS

Care must be taken to <u>avoid</u> using <u>products</u> that are <u>harmful</u> <u>to</u> <u>people</u>, <u>animals</u>, and <u>plant life.</u> Small components in toys can be swallowed by children. Paints that have lead are also dangerous. <u>Harmful waste</u> needs to be disposed of carefully and in appropriate containers.

Examiner's Top Tip
Always include environmental considerations when designing and making.

QUICK TEST

1. Give two examples of materials that can be recycled.
2. Is a metal a renewable or non-renewable resource?
3. What are biodegradable materials?
4. Which timbers are more environmentally friendly: hardwoods or softwoods?

4. Softwoods.
3. Materials which decompose quickly and are not harmful to the environment.
2. Non-renewable.
1. Paper, card, metals, thermoplastics.

USE OF CAD

CAD stands for **computer-aided** **design**. CAD is widely used in **schools** **and** **industry**. CAD is particularly good for producing **working** **drawings** and **three-dimensional** **computer** **models**. These can be used in **school** **projects**.

Examiner's Top Tip
Know the advantages of using CAD for school-based projects.

COMPUTER-AIDED DESIGN

CAD **systems** are used in schools for a **range** **of** **applications**. These are:
• **2-D and 3-D drawings**
• **solid models of the project**
• **materials databases.**

Some **CAD** **systems** allow designs to be automatically **downloaded** to **computer-aided** **machines.** This eliminates the need to program the machine before machining can commence.

ADVANTAGES OF CAD

Even though CAD systems are relatively <u>expensive</u> they have a number of <u>advantages</u> over manual drawing methods:
· They produce high-quality and consistent drawings.
· Information can be stored easily.
· Standard parts can be held in a parts library reducing the time it takes to draw them.
· Once people are used to the systems CAD can be quicker than drawing complex assemblies by hand.
· Changes to a drawing can be easily made.
· Many packages will automatically dimension components.
· Solid modelling allows the product to be rotated and viewed from a number of angles.

CAD should not be a total substitute for sketching as a design tool. <u>Freehand</u> <u>sketching</u> is quick, allows freedom of thought and is especially suitable for work in the initial design and development stages.

OTHER BENEFITS OF CAD
Many computer packages allow <u>images</u> to be <u>scanned</u> into the system and <u>photographs</u> to be <u>imported</u>. This can help in many areas of project work.
<u>Plotter</u> <u>cutters</u> are used for cutting out shapes in sheet material and <u>engraving</u> <u>machines</u> can be used to produce flat models of a product.

TYPES OF DRAWINGS

These include <u>pictorial</u>, <u>exploded</u> and <u>orthographic</u> drawings. <u>Pictorial</u> <u>drawings</u> give the most realistic idea of the product. They can be easily drawn using <u>solid-modelling</u> packages. <u>Exploded</u> <u>drawings</u> show how the product fits together. They are useful to show how a product will <u>assemble</u> during <u>manufacture</u>. <u>Orthographic</u> <u>drawings</u> are working drawings which are used when manufacturing the product. They contain all the <u>necessary</u> <u>dimensions</u>. They can be drawn using 2-D CAD packages.

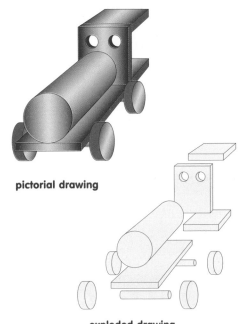

pictorial drawing

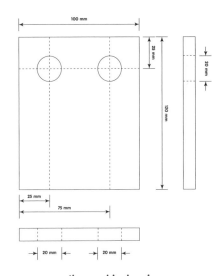

exploded drawing

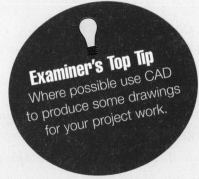

orthographic drawing

SYSTEMS AND CONTROL DESIGN

Systems diagrams are a common way of describing systems. Systems diagrams can be used to show how the parts of a product are linked together.
They can also be used to show how products and parts flow through a manufacturing system.
Common systems components that produce movements are levers, gears, cams and belt drives.

SYSTEM DIAGRAMS

Systems consist of a number of parts, components or processes that work together to achieve an output.
A system can be broken down into a number of elements each of which can be represented by a block diagram.
Each system block has an input, performs an operation and has an output.

input → | control / operation | → output

CLOSED-LOOP AND OPEN-LOOP SYSTEMS

An open-loop system is one where there is no feedback to help control the system. The accuracy of open-loop systems depends upon how well the system has been set up before it is operated.
Closed-loop systems have sensors that can sense the output values of the system. The sensors feed back information to the input and change the input values if necessary.

OPEN-LOOP SYSTEM

speed →
feed → | lathe or milling machine | → output depends upon accuracy of settings
cut →

CLOSED-LOOP SYSTEM

feed
speed → | lathe or milling machine | → machine output
cut

feed sensor
speed sensor
depth of cut sensor

CLOSED-LOOP SYSTEMS

These are found in a number of situations.
An example is in the control of CNC lathes and milling machines.
When manual machines are used, the depth of cut, feed rate and speeds are set by the operator. The quality of the finish will depend upon how these have been set before the machines starts to cut. If the finish is poor the operator will have to manually re-adjust the controls to improve the quality of the finish.
Many computer-operated machines are able to make these adjustments automatically when the machine is cutting. Sensors are used to monitor depth of cut, feed rate and speed. If the cutter, for example, hits a hard spot in the material or the depth of cut is too great, the sensor will measure this and adjust the controls automatically. This can lead to better finishes.

THE PRODUCTION PROCESS AS A SYSTEM

A <u>manufacturing process</u> transforms a material or product from one shape to another. A <u>system</u> <u>diagram</u> can be used to show how a manufacturing system <u>links</u> <u>together</u> all parts of the manufacturing process.

<u>Feedback</u> <u>loops</u> can be built into manufacturing systems to make them more effective. For example, quality checks can be made at various points. If faults are found in the process the operation can be stopped and appropriate adjustments made.

Quality monitoring in this way can be shown by including feedback loops into the manufacturing system diagram.

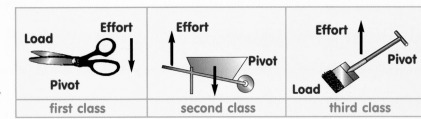

making axle for a toy car

round bar → saw → machine/ lathe → drill holes for split pin

making axle for a toy car

round bar → saw → machine/ lathe → quality check → drill holes for split pin

reject machine

SYSTEM COMPONENTS

LEVERS

The <u>leverage</u> <u>principle</u> is commonly used for a number of applications. Levers can be classified as first-class, second-class and third-class levers.

first class	second class	third class
Load / Effort / Pivot	Effort / Pivot / Load	Effort / Pivot / Load

GEARS

These are used to transmit motion between shafts which are relatively close together. A simple <u>gear</u> <u>train</u> consists of two meshing gears. Here the shafts will turn in opposite directions. An idler gear can be used in a simple gear train to make the gears turn in the same direction.

A <u>compound</u> <u>gear</u> <u>train</u> has more than two gears in a system.

<u>Bevel</u> <u>gears</u> are used to turn shafts which are at right angles to each other.

<u>Worm</u> <u>gears</u> and <u>worm</u> <u>wheels</u> are widely used in gear boxes.

<u>Rack</u> <u>and</u> <u>pinions</u> are gears used to changed rotary motion into linear motion.

simple gear train

compound gear train

bevel gears

rack and pinion gears

spur gears

worm gears

BELT DRIVES

These are used to transmit motion and power between shafts which are relatively far apart. The shafts will rotate in the same direction unless the belts are crossed. The belts can have flat, round or vee cross-sections.

<u>Toothed</u> <u>belts</u> are used where no splippage of the belt should occur.

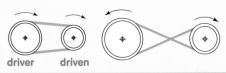

driver   driven

CAMS

These change rotary motion into linear motion. The <u>cam</u> <u>follower</u> is in contact with the surface of the cam and producing <u>reciprocating</u> <u>movement</u>.

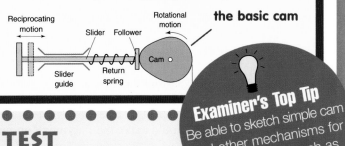

the basic cam

Reciprocating motion — Slider — Follower — Rotational motion — Cam — Slider guide — Return spring

Examiner's Top Tip
Be able to sketch simple cam and other mechanisms for simple projects such as children's toys.

QUICK TEST

1. What is a system?
2. What are the three elements of a block diagram?
3. What type of control includes sensors – open-loop or closed-loop?
4. What is the purpose of gears?
5. What do cams do?
6. Why are bevel gears used?
7. Why are crossed belts used on pulley systems?

7. So that pulley shafts will rotate in opposite directions.
6. To turn shafts at right angles to each other.
5. Change rotary motion into linear motion.
4. To transmit motion between shafts which are close together.
3. Closed-loop.
2. Input, transformation (work done), output.
1. A number of parts, components or processes that work together to give an output.

EXAM QUESTIONS — Use the questions to test your progress. Check your answers on page 94.

1. A café requires a set of stands to hold its menus.

   Thirty stands are required.

   Give three specification points for the stand. (3 marks)

   ....

   ....

2. When the handle of the animal toy face is pushed and pulled the
   wings move as indicated.

   a) What type of motion is made by the handle? (1 mark)

   ....

   ....

   b) What type of motion is made by the wing? (1 mark)

   ....

   ....

   c) Which is the input motion and which is the output motion? (1 mark)

   ....

   ....

   d) What type of mechanism could be used to make the wings move? (1 mark)

   ....

   ....

3. A manufacturer needs to produce a desk tidy as shown.

   a) State two things you would have to find out before
      starting the design. (2 marks)

   ....

   ....

   b) Why may the solution be a poor design? (1 mark)

   ....

   ....

4. The diagram shows a wooden toy where the flag moves up and
   down when it is pulled along.

   a) What mechanism would make the flag move up quickly and
      then down slowly? (1 mark)

   ....

   ....

   b) State two advantages of this type of mechanism. (2 marks)

   ....

   ....

5. a) What does CAD stand for? (1 mark)

....

....

b) Describe two ways in which CAD could be used in the design of products. (2 marks)

....

....

6. Give three ways in which products can be tested against a specification. (3 marks)

....

7. What is the advantage to the environment of using plastic products which are suitable for recycling?

(1 mark)

....

8. Many products are designed for planned obsolescence. Describe two effects that this may have on the

design of a product. (2 marks)

....

....

9. A self-assembly book rack is made from chipboard covered in veneer and joined together using knock-down

fittings. Describe two ways in which the book rack makes use of materials in an environmentally-friendly

way. (2 marks)

....

10. Explain two safety issues that a designer should be aware of when designing for young children. (2 marks)

....

11. Both wooden and plastic patio seats are available at a supermarket.

a) State two reasons why a consumer might choose to buy a wooden chair. (2 marks)

....

....

b) State two reasons why a consumer might choose to buy a plastic chair. (2 marks)

....

....

12 State two safety features that need to be considered when designing lighting. (2 marks)

....

How did you do?

1–3	correct	.................start again
4–6	correct	.................getting there
7–9	correct	.................good work
10–12	correct	.................excellent

SAFE WORKING PROCEDURES

Safety is an **important** **factor** in all areas of Design and Technology. This includes:
Safety **in** **the** **workshop** when working with materials, hand tools and machines
Being aware of **safety** **regulations** and codes for school workshops and industry
Considering safety aspects when **designing** **products**.

SAFETY IN THE WORKSHOP

SAFE WORKING PROCEDURES

- *Always wear the correct protective clothing to protect eyes, body and feet.*
- *Tie loose hair back.*
- *Make sure that you understand how to use the tools and equipment properly.*
- *Make sure that you use the right tool for the job.*
- *Use the guards on the machines.*
- *Never leave chuck keys in the machines.*
- *Keep hands away from moving parts and cutters.*
- *Never clean swarf away with bare hands.*
- *Never adjust or clean a machine without switching it off at the isolator.*
- *Do not leave machines unattended whilst in use.*

SAFE USE OF MATERIALS

- *Handle materials properly and with care.*
- *Never work without adequate ventilation.*
- *Protect eyes from dust, particles and dangerous liquids and substances.*
- *Protect hands from potential skin hazards.*
- *Use protective gloves or barrier cream.*
- *Keep flammable materials from naked flames.*
- *Wear protective gloves when handling hot or sharp materials.*
- *Remove burrs from materials.*
- *Dispose of waste properly.*

SAFETY IN THE WORKSHOP
This involves:
- *safe use of materials*
- *safe working procedures when using machinery, tools and equipment*
- *general safety in the workshop.*

Examiner's Top Tip
Know the safety procedures for operations in the workshop.

SAFETY WITH OTHERS

- *Move around safely in the workshop.*
- *Never run or fool around.*
- *Carry tools safely.*
- *Never work on machines without permission.*
- *Take care to protect others from hot materials, fumes, dust and dangerous liquids.*
- *Report all accidents, breakages and faults.*
- *Keep the workshop tidy.*
- *Know the positions of the emergency stop buttons and first aid boxes .*

SAFETY IN PRODUCT DESIGN

Safety is a main consideration in the design of products.

When designing products care should be taken to ensure that products are <u>safe to use</u>. <u>Toxic paints and materials</u> should be avoided especially in <u>products designed for children</u>. Products should be designed with <u>smooth corners, edges and shapes</u> so that users cannot cut themselves.

SAFETY STANDARDS

The <u>British Standards Institute (BSI)</u> has developed <u>safety standards</u> for a wide range of products. The <u>BSI kite mark</u> is an indication that the product has met the safety standards. Many of the products have gone through <u>rigorous tests</u>. These include paints, children's toys and equipment and electrical goods. <u>British Standards</u> can be used to help select the correct materials and equipment for products.

RISK ANALYSIS

<u>Risk analysis</u> is carried out in school workshops and industry to <u>reduce the potential risks</u> when using <u>hazardous substances</u>, <u>equipment</u> and <u>machinery</u>. The risk associated with each operation is assessed and precautions to minimise the risk implemented. Schools and industries will have <u>codes of practice</u> that have to be observed.

REGULATIONS

There are a number of regulations and codes of practice which relate to safety in the workplace. These include <u>COSHH (Control Of Substances Hazardous to Health)</u> regulations and the <u>Safety at Work Act</u>.

QUICK TEST

1. What are three general areas of safety which should be observed in workshops?
2. What does the BSI kite mark indicate?
3. Why is risk analysis carried out?
4. What does COSHH stand for?

1. Safe use of materials; safe working procedures with machines, tools and equipment; general safety in workshop.
2. Indication that a product has met safety standards.
3. To reduce the potential risks when using hazardous substances, equipment or machinery.
4. Control Of Substances Hazardous to Health.

THE NEED FOR MARKING OUT

Accurate **marking** **out** is required to:

• **Define** **the** **shape** of the outline of the article to be made

• **Indicate the** **positions** **of** **holes** and other features

• **Help keep** **waste** to a **minimum**.

All measurements should **start** **from** **a** **datum** surface or datum line.

Datums are machined, filed or planed surfaces and lines.

Examiner's Top Tip
Remember to always take measurements from datum face or datum side when marking out.

MARKING OUT

MARKING OUT FOR WOOD

A <u>face</u> <u>side</u> should be planed first to give a smooth surface to the wood. A <u>face</u> <u>edge</u> can then be planed square to this side. These give the <u>initial</u> <u>datum</u> <u>surface</u>. All subsequent marking out can then be carried out relative to the face side and face edge. A <u>try</u> <u>square</u> is used as an aid to marking out lines at right angles to the surface. It is also used to check the <u>squareness</u> <u>of</u> <u>the</u> <u>sides</u> of the wood. A sharp pencil can be used to mark the lines. Where lines are required to be made <u>across</u> <u>the</u> <u>grain</u> for sawing or chiselling a <u>marking</u> <u>knife</u> is used.

The <u>waste</u> <u>side</u> of the material should be clearly marked by <u>shading</u> with a pencil.

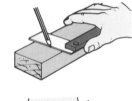

Marking <u>gauges</u> can be used to mark lines <u>parallel</u> to either a face side or face edge.

marking gauge

MARKING OUT FOR METAL

<u>Datum</u> <u>surfaces</u> <u>or</u> <u>edges</u> should first be made either by <u>filing</u> or by <u>milling</u> or <u>turning</u>. A <u>scriber</u> is used against an engineer's square to mark lines parallel to the datum surfaces.

<u>Marking</u> <u>blue</u> can be applied to the surface of shiny metals to show the scriber lines. Where the surface is to be machined light centre punch marks are made along the line so it can be seen during machining operations where coolants are being used.

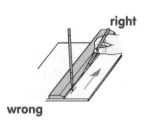

right

wrong

a scriber

A <u>surface</u> <u>plate</u> can be used to provide an <u>accurate</u> <u>surface</u> for the marking out. The datum face is placed on the table. Lines parallel to the block are marked using a scribing block. <u>Angle</u> <u>plates</u> enable components to be held at right angles to the surface plate.

<u>Round</u> <u>bars</u> can be marked out with the aid of a <u>vee</u> <u>block</u> and <u>clamp</u>.

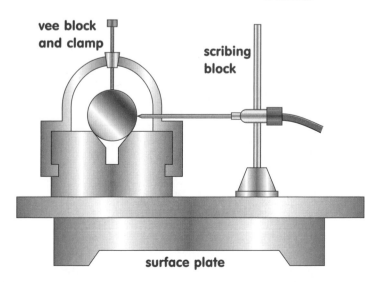

vee block and clamp

scribing block

surface plate

OTHER MARKING TOOLS

<u>Dividers</u> are used for marking circles and arcs.

<u>Scribers</u> are used to mark lines on metals and plastics.

<u>Odd-leg</u> <u>callipers</u> mark lines parallel to a datum surface.

<u>Centre</u> <u>squares</u> are used to find the centre of a round bar.

<u>Bevel</u> <u>gauges</u> are used to mark off angles on wood or metal.

PREPARATION FOR MANUFACTURE

PLASTICS

For <u>plastics</u> mark off with a <u>wax</u> <u>crayon</u> or fine <u>felt-tipped</u> <u>pen</u>.
A <u>scriber</u> can be used for marking lines which have to be cut.
All the main tools used for marking out metals can be used with
plastics. The only exceptions are the ones that might scratch the
surface of the plastics. <u>Scratches</u> can be a source of weakness
for many plastics, especially if they are brittle.

Examiner's Top Tip
Be able to describe stages of marking out parts in wood, plastics or metals using correct tools.

QUICK TEST

1. What tool is used with a try square to mark out wood across the grain?
2. What is a marking gauge used for?
3. What type of face or edge should marking out be carried out from?
4. How can lines on metal be seen more clearly during machining?
5. What are dividers used for?
6. What are centre squares used for?
7. What can be used to mark plastics where they are not to be scratched?

7. Wax crayon or felt-tipped pen.
6. Finding the centres of round bars.
5. Drawing circles or arcs.
4. By lightly centre-punching.
3. A datum.
2. Marking lines parallel to grain on wood.
1. Marking knife.

HAND TOOLS FOR METALS AND PLASTICS

Hand tools include **hacksaws**, **files** and **taps and dies**.
Many **hand tools** can be used for both **metals** and **plastics**.
Care should be taken to use the **correct tool for the job**.
The correct **safety precautions** should be **observed** when using tools.
Care should be taken to keep the tools in a **good working condition**.

FILES

Files are specified by their <u>cut</u>, <u>grade</u>, <u>cross-section</u> and <u>length</u>.
The <u>teeth</u> of a file may either be <u>single-cut</u> or <u>double-cut</u>.
<u>Double-cut</u> files are used for most <u>general plastics</u> and <u>metalwork</u>.
<u>Single-cut</u> files are used for <u>hard metals</u>.

single-cut

double-cut

GRADE OF FILES	USE
Rough	soft metals and plastics
Second-cut	roughing out hard metals and plastics and finishing soft metals and plastics
Smooth	finishing cuts and draw-filing

SAFETY FIRST
<u>Use the correct size handle</u> for the file in use.
<u>Never use a file without its handle.</u>
<u>Always use a file to take off the sharp burrs</u> made by machining processes (deburring).

CROSS-SECTIONS

Flat	▬	*used for general work*
Square	▯	*used for finishing square and rectangular holes and slots.*
Three square	▲	*a triangular file used for filing out sharp corners and internal angles.*
Round	◉	*used for filing out holes.*

dreadnought

<u>Dreadnought</u> files are used for filing soft metals, typically aluminium castings.

<u>Needle</u> files are small files used for precise and accurate work.

needle files

PRACTICAL POINTS

<u>Clogged up</u> (pinned) files can be cleaned up using a <u>file card</u>.
To prevent pinning <u>chalk</u> can be rubbed onto the <u>face of the file</u>.
<u>New files</u> should be used on <u>plastics</u> and <u>soft metals</u> such as copper, aluminium and bronze.
Then in turn on <u>harder materials</u> such as steels and cast irons.

<u>Draw-filing</u> can be used to provide a <u>smooth finish</u>. <u>Emery cloth</u> can then be wrapped around the file to remove the last remaining file marks.

Examiner's Top Tip
Be able to describe how parts of products are cut out and finished by hand.

COLD CHISELS

Cold chisels are mainly used for removing metal. With care they can be used on some of the tougher plastics materials.

Types of cold chisel	Uses
Flat	cutting sheet metal, cutting grooves and chiselling flat surfaces
Cross-cut	cutting narrow grooves and keyways
Diamond point	cleaning corners

SAWS

Hacksaws are use for sawing metals and plastics. The blade of a hacksaw can be turned on its side to allow long cuts to be made.

Junior hacksaws are smaller versions of the hacksaw. However the blade cannot be turned on its side. Junior hacksaws or used for smaller pieces of work.

The teeth on hacksaw blades face forward so that they cut on the forward stroke.

The number of teeth per centimetre varies from 5 to 12 depending upon the type of work and material being cut. For soft metals and plastics a coarse blade should be used. For hard metals a finer blade should be used.

Material	Solid block	Tube and thin sheet
Iron and steels	6–7 teeth/cm	12 teeth/cm
Plastics and non-ferrous metals	5–6 teeth/cm	8–10 teeth/cm

Coping saws are used for cutting curves in metal and plastics. The teeth of a coping saw point backwards so that it cuts on the backward stroke. This prevents the blade from buckling and breaking when cutting.

Abrafiles have circular teeth. The blade can be fitted into a hacksaw frame. Abrafiles are generally used for sheet metal and plastics work.

coping saw

QUICK TEST

1. How are files specified?
2. What is meant by pinning?
3. What is draw-filing used for?
4. What is a dreadnought file used for?
5. Which way should the blades of a hacksaw face?
6. What is a coping saw used for?
7. What are abrafiles used for?
8. What are the three types of taps?

1. By their cut, grade, cross-section and length.
2. Clogging up of a file.
3. To finish work.
4. On soft materials such as aluminium castings.
5. Forward.
6. Cutting around curved shapes.
7. Cutting sheet metals or plastics.
8. Taper, second, plug.

HAND TOOLS FOR WOOD

WOOD-CUTTING TOOLS

Hand tools for wood include tenon saws, ripsaws, cross-cut saws, wood chisels and hand drills.

Wood tools need to be sharpened regularly.

The teeth on saw blades face forward. The exception is the coping saw where they face backwards.

The correct safety precautions must be observed when using wood tools such as chisels and saws.

SAWS

Ripsaws and cross-cut saws are two types of hand saws. They are used for cutting large pieces of wood and sheets. Ripsaws are used for cutting in the direction of the grain.

Cross-cut saws are used for cutting across the grain. They are also good for cutting man-made boards.

Tenon saws are used for cutting small pieces of wood. Tenon saws are a type of backsaw. Dovetail saws are used for cutting dovetails and small tenons.

Coping saws can be used to cut curves.

WOOD CHISELS

mortice chisel

bevel-edged

firmer

SAFETY FIRST
When using chisels always make sure that both hands are behind the front of the chisel when cutting.

Types of chisel	Use
Firmer chisel	Used for general work. Has a square edge to the blade. Available in sizes from 3–50 mm.
Mortice chisel	These have a thicker blade than firmer chisels. They are designed to be used with a mallet and can withstand heavy blows.
Bevel-edged chisel	These are used for cutting wood from the corners of joints and other awkward places.

PLANES

Jack planes are used for planing wood *flat and to size*.
Smoothing planes are used for *finishing* and *planing end grain*.
To ensure high-quality work the blades need to be kept sharp and should be adjusted correctly.

To avoid *splitting the grain* when planing across the grain, pieces of wood can be *clamped* across the edges of the wood. This ensures that the grain is squeezed together.

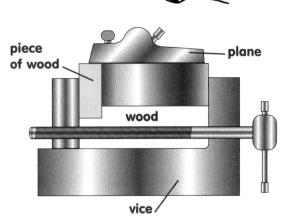

piece of wood — plane

wood

vice

SPECIAL PURPOSE PLANES

Shoulder planes – for finishing shoulders in wood
Plough planes – for cutting grooves
Rebate planes – for producing rebates
Spokeshaves – used for curves.

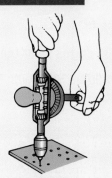

Surforms are used to remove material rapidly. The blade is replaceable and can either be standard or fine.

DRILLS

hand drill   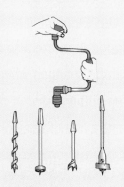 **brace and bits**    **hole saw**

Examiner's Top Tip
Know how to use wood tools safely – especially chisels.

Examiner's Top Tip
When describing how tools are used to make things make sure you use the right tool for the right purpose.

QUICK TEST

1. What are ripsaws used for?
2. Name three types of wood chisel.
3. What is a jack plane used for?
4. How can splitting of the wood be prevented when planing across the grain?
5. What is a spokeshave used for?

1. Cutting large pieces of wood in the direction of the grain.
2. Firmer, mortice and bevel-edged.
3. Planing wood flat and to size.
4. By clamping pieces of wood across the edges.
5. Planing curved surfaces.

MACHINE TOOLS FOR METALS AND PLASTICS

CUTTING AND SHAPING TOOLS

Machine tools are power-driven machines that are used for cutting and shaping materials.

Machine tools produce smooth, accurate finishes at faster rates than hand tools.

Because metal and plastics machine tool processes are wasting operations, material is lost in the form of chippings and swarf.

Many machine tools are now operated with the aid of computer control.

SAFETY FIRST

When using all machine tools goggles must be worn, long hair tied back, sleeves should be rolled up. Ties should not be worn unless secured with a tie clip.

work

vice

Work for drilling should be clamped either in a machine vice, hand vice or by using clamps and packing. Round work can be held using vee blocks and clamps.

LATHE TOOLS

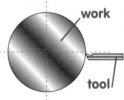
work
centre line
tool

Most lathe tools are made from high speed steel.

Tungsten carbide and ceramic-tipped tools are also used. These tips can be changed when the cutting edges wear out.

The cutting point of the tool should be level with the centre line of the work.

DRILLING

Pillar drills are used to drill holes in metals or plastics. The drills are held in a machine chuck. When an accurate hole is required the hole is finished off using a reamer. Most twist drill bits are made from high-speed steel.

The drill point angle for most metals is 118 degrees. For plastics a modified drill point angle of 140 degrees can be used.

The drilling speed will depend upon the material being drilled. Aluminium, for example, can be drilled at a faster speed than mild steel. The correct cutting speeds can be found in engineers' reference books.

Other drills included countersink drills, counterboring drills and hole saws.

countersink   **counterboring tool**   **hole saw**

CENTRE LATHE

Centre lathes are used mainly for producing cylindrical surfaces. Common turning operations are:

• *turning down the bar*

• *facing off a bar*

• *drilling*

• *parting off.*

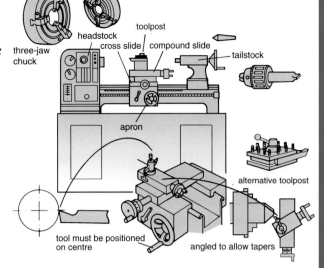

four-jaw chuck
headstock
toolpost
cross slide | compound slide
three-jaw chuck
tailstock
apron
alternative toolpost
tool must be positioned on centre
angled to allow tapers

PARTS OF THE LATHE

<u>Headstock</u> – *contains gears, motor and drive mechanism and holds the workpiece chuck.*

<u>Tailstock</u> – *can be used to support one end of work when turning and hold tools such as drills and reamers.*

<u>Carriage</u> – *slides along bed.*

<u>Toolpost</u> – *holds the lathe tools.*

<u>Three-jaw</u> <u>chucks</u> *are used for* <u>round</u> <u>and</u> <u>hexagonal</u> *work.* <u>Four-jaw</u> <u>chucks</u> *are used for* <u>square</u> *and* <u>other</u> <u>shapes</u>. *In the four-jaw chuck each of the jaws operates independently and so the work has to be 'centred' prior to machining.*

MILLING MACHINES

Milling can produce flat surfaces much more quickly and more accurately than by hand. The two main types of milling machines are the <u>vertical</u> <u>milling</u> <u>machine</u> and the <u>horizontal</u> <u>milling</u> <u>machine</u>. Work for both should be clamped securely to the machine bed either by clamps or using a machine vice.

COOLANTS

<u>Coolants</u> are used to <u>reduce</u> <u>the</u> <u>heat</u> generated and to <u>reduce</u> <u>the</u> <u>friction</u> on many operations. In the case of plastics, because of their low thermal conductivity, a coolant such as soapy water should be used to keep the material cool.

Examiner's Top Tip
Be able to briefly describe the stages of making a part of a design using machines.

QUICK TEST

1. What safety precautions must be observed when using machines?
2. How should work for drilling be held?
3. What are four-jaw lathe chucks used for?
4. What are milling machines used for?
5. Name a material used for lathe tools.
6. What drill angles can be used for drilling plastics?

6. 118 or 140 degrees.
5. High-speed steel, tungsten carbide, ceramic.
4. Machining flat surfaces.
3. Holding square bar.
2. Machine vice, hand vice or clamps and packing.
1. Wear goggles, long hair tied back, no loose clothing, no ties unless the clip used.

MACHINE TOOLS FOR WOOD

SAFETY FIRST

SAFETY FIRST

You will be very unlikely to use a <u>bandsaw</u> or <u>circular</u> <u>saw</u> in the school workshop. They are, however, used by trained teachers and technicians to cut and prepare a whole range of <u>timber</u> <u>shapes</u> <u>and</u> <u>sections</u>. They are also widely used in industry.

<u>Extreme</u> <u>caution</u> must be taken when using the machines.

<u>Goggles</u> should be worn on all machines which are not fully enclosed.

The <u>dust</u> from wood machining is a <u>health</u> <u>hazard</u>, especially from <u>man-made</u> <u>boards</u>. Good <u>dust</u> <u>extraction</u> is essential. <u>Face</u> <u>masks</u> should be work for <u>dusty</u> <u>operations</u>.

Band saws are used to cut curves and other shapes. They can also be used to cut plastics and wood. Narrow blades can be fitted to cut out intricate shapes.

guard removed for clarity

Circular saws can be used for cutting large sheets.

The wood-turning lathe is used for turning round pieces of work. The work is generally held on a faceplate.

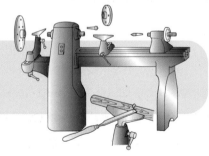

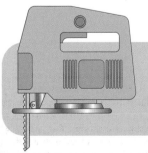

Electric jig saws are portable pieces of equipment which can be used to cut around curved shapes in sheet materials. The jig saw has a short blade which reciprocates and cuts the wood at high speed.

CUTTING AND SHAPING TOOLS

Wood machines are used for cutting large sheets, making shapes and finishing off work.

They range from circular saws, band saws, wood turning lathes, jig saws, sanding machines and CNC routers.

Machines speed up the production process and give an accurate finish to products.

Many woodworking machines are potentially dangerous and should only be used by trained operators.

Examiner's Top Tip
Remember safety hazards when machining man-made boards.

CNC ROUTERS

Computer-controlled routing machines are used widely in machining wood-based products. They give an accurate finish. They can be programmed to machine intricate shapes and can be used to produce batches of products with identical measurements. They speed up the production process. The work tends to be fully enclosed in a cabinet which has dust extraction.

The grain structure of natural timbers can cause problems when machining. When cutting in different directions some of the wood can rip and cause poor finishes. Man-made boards such as MDF is better since there are no directional problems with the material.

Examiner's Top Tip
Be able to compare the advantages of CNC to manual machines.

QUICK TEST

1. Name two types of wood machine.
2. What are circular saws used for?
3. What is the main safety hazard when machining MDF?
4. What are jig saws used for?
5. What are the advantages of using CNC routers?

1. Band saw, circular saw, wood turning lathes, sanding machine, jig saws, CNC routing machines.
2. To cut large sheets and sections.
3. Potentially harmful dust is produced.
4. To cut out shapes in sheet materials.
5. Give an accurate finish, are quick, can be programmed to machine intricate shapes.

CASTING AND MOULDING

Reforming is where the metal changes state during the manufacturing process.
Metal-reforming methods include sand casting, die casting and investment casting.
Casting involves pouring metals into a mould either by force or by gravity.
Moulds can be either temporary or permanent.
Sand casting and investment casting are temporary moulding processes.
Die casting is an example of a permanent processes.

SAND CASTING

Sand casting is the most frequently used casting process. Sand is moulded by hand or machine around a wooden or metal pattern. This can be withdrawn leaving a cavity of the required shape in the mould. Most moulds are made in two halves to aid the mould-making process. The molten metal is poured into the runner. Risers

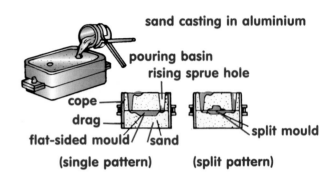

sand casting in aluminium

pouring basin
rising sprue hole
cope
drag
flat-sided mould / sand
split mould
(single pattern)   (split pattern)

allow air and gases to escape during casting. The size and shape of the pattern must take into account the amount of shrinkage that will occur during solidification. The finished castings are fettled to remove excess metal.

ADVANTAGES OF SAND CASTING
- Low cost method of producing general castings
- Cost-effective for low production volumes
- Pattern can be re-used.

DISADVANTAGES OF SAND CASTING
- Not as accurate as die or investment casting
- Needs finishing
- The sand mould needs to be made for each product.

Sand casting is used with:
- cast iron   • steel   • brass   • aluminium   • magnesium-based alloys.

INVESTMENT CASTING

Investment casting is also called the lost wax process. It can be used in the casting of jewellery and for producing components that are difficult to die-cast, forge or machine. Investment castings have good surface finishes and good dimensional accuracy. The process involves making a wax pattern with a feed system. The pattern is dipped in a refractory ceramic slurry (called investing). This produces a hard casing around the wax. The wax is then heated and drained out of the ceramic shell. The molten metal can then be poured into the shell and left to solidify. The ceramic shell is then broken away from the casting.

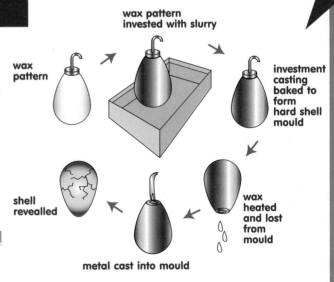

wax pattern
wax pattern
invested with slurry
investment casting baked to form hard shell mould
wax heated and lost from mould
metal cast into mould
shell revealled

HIGH-PRESSURE DIE CASTING

High-pressure die casting is used with low melting point alloys such as aluminium and zinc-based alloys. In high-pressure die casting the molten metal is forced into a metal die at high pressure. The metal solidifies quickly due to water cooling. When cooled the dies are opened and the casting is automatically ejected from the die. High-pressure die casting is used in a wide range of applications including toy cars, car door handles, parts for kitchen equipment, car parts and gear box casings.

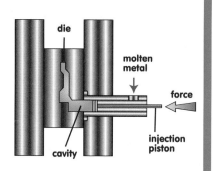

ADVANTAGES
- Produces accurate castings
- Good surface finish
- Little finishing required
- Relatively low costs for large volumes.

DISADVANTAGES
- Not suitable for small batches
- Cost of buying the equipment is high
- Cost of dies can be high
- Can only be used for low melting point alloys.

Examiner's Top Tip
Be able to describe casting processes with the aid of simple diagrams.

REFORMING METALS

Examiner's Top Tip
Know the advantages and disadvantages of sand and die casting.

GRAVITY DIE CASTING

In gravity die casting the metal is poured into metal dies. It is mainly used for magnesium-based and zinc-based alloys. The finish tends to be better than sand castings. Typical products include car cylinder heads, wheel hubs, disc brake parts and pistons.

QUICK TEST

1. What metals can sand casting be used for?
2. What are the advantages of sand casting?
3. What are the advantages of investment processes?
4. What metals is high-pressure die casting used for?
5. What products are made by gravity die casting?
6. What are the advantages of die casting?

1. Cast iron, steel, brass, aluminium, magnesium alloys.
2. Low cost, cost-effective for low volumes, pattern can be re-used.
3. Good dimensional accuracy, good surface finish.
4. Zinc and aluminium alloys.
5. Car cylinder heads, wheel hubs, disc brake parts and pistons.
6. Accurate castings, good surface finish, little finishing required, low cost for large volumes.

REFORMING PLASTICS

MOULDINGS AND EXTRUSIONS

The reforming of plastics includes injection moulding, extrusion, compression moulding and monomer casting. Reforming processes are used in industry for the production of a wide range of plastic products.

Injection moulding and extrusion are used to process thermoplastics.

Compression moulding and transfer moulding are used to process thermosetting plastics.

INJECTION MOULDING

Injection moulding is used to produce a variety of thermoplastic components. Due to the high cost of the machines and the dies the process is only suitable for long production runs. Products include plastic spoons, model aircraft, telephones, buckets, bowls and parts for household goods.

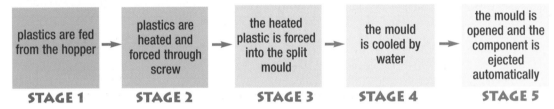

plastics are fed from the hopper	plastics are heated and forced through screw	the heated plastic is forced into the split mould	the mould is cooled by water	the mould is opened and the component is ejected automatically
STAGE 1	**STAGE 2**	**STAGE 3**	**STAGE 4**	**STAGE 5**

ADVANTAGES OF INJECTION MOULDING
Good surface finish
Products can be coloured
Relatively cheap process once equipment has been bought
Components can be made quickly
Little finishing required
Components can be made accurately
Less energy used than similar metal-processing operations

DISADVANTAGES
Cost of machines and tools high
No good for low production runs

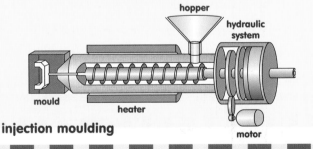

injection moulding

MONOMER CASTING

This is a low-cost method for making products such as chess pieces, toy soldiers and garden ornaments. The process can be used for both thermo- and thermosetting plastics. The starting material must be liquid enough to pour. The plastic is poured into an open mould. The product can then be removed once the plastic has set.

Examiner's Top Tip
Be able to describe the stages of reforming processes with the aid of block diagrams.

PLASTIC EXTRUSION

Extrusion is used to produce articles with a _constant cross-section_. Extrusion is a _continuous process_ where a heated thermoplastic is pushed through a _die_. The die has the shape of the required cross-section. _Extrusion is used to produce _plastic_ _curtain_ _rails_ and, _window_ _frames_. Also _plastic_ _rods_ and _tubes_ in a range of _standard sizes_.

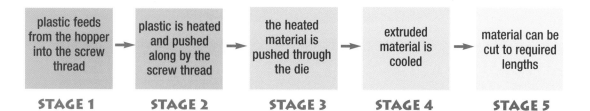

extrusion moulding

STAGE 1	STAGE 2	STAGE 3	STAGE 4	STAGE 5
plastic feeds from the hopper into the screw thread	plastic is heated and pushed along by the screw thread	the heated material is pushed through the die	extruded material is cooled	material can be cut to required lengths

MOULDING

COMPRESSION MOULDING

Compression _moulding_ is used on _thermosets_ with minimal waste. It is used to produce components such as _car_ _distributor_ _caps_, _camera_ _cases_, _handles_, _knobs_, _electrical_ _plugs_ and _sockets_. The _cure_ _times_ for the process vary between 0.5 and 3 minutes.

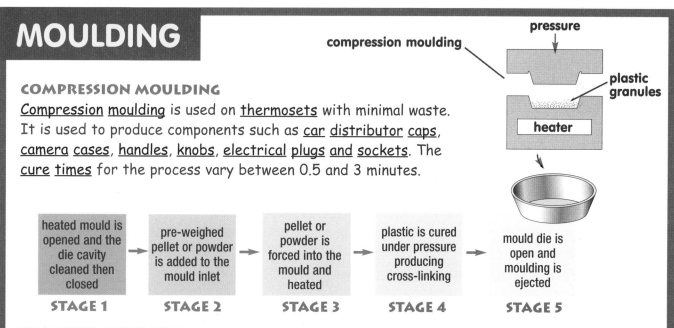

compression moulding

STAGE 1	STAGE 2	STAGE 3	STAGE 4	STAGE 5
heated mould is opened and the die cavity cleaned then closed	pre-weighed pellet or powder is added to the mould inlet	pellet or powder is forced into the mould and heated	plastic is cured under pressure producing cross-linking	mould die is open and moulding is ejected

TRANSFER MOULDING

This is an _alternative_ _process_ for the production of _thermosetting_ _plastics_. Cycle times are shorter than with compression moulding due to _faster_ _heating_ _and_ _curing_ _times_. _Closer_ _tolerances_ are possible than with compression moulding.
Parts include _kitchen_ _utensil_ _handles_, _electrical_ _appliance_ _parts_, _electronic_ _components_ and _electrical_ _plug_ _parts_.

QUICK TEST

1. What types of plastics are injection moulded?
2. State three advantages of injection moulding.
3. What type of process produces a constant cross-section?
4. What components can be produced using compression moulding?
5. What type of low-cost process is often used for making chess pieces?
6. Why do thermosetting plastics have to be compression-moulded?

1. Thermoplastics.
2. Form good surface finish, can be coloured, cheap process, quick, little finishing, accurate, less energy than similar metal processes.
3. Extrusion.
4. Electrical plugs, sockets, car distributor caps, handles and knobs.
5. Monomer casting.
6. They need a curing cycle.

DEFORMING WOOD, METALS AND PLASTICS

CHANGING THE SHAPE OF MATERIALS

- Deforming materials refer to processes that bring about a change in shape without a loss of material.
- Deforming of metals include bending of sheet metals and pipework, pressings and deep drawing.
- Deforming of plastics includes line bending, vacuum forming and blow moulding.
- Deforming of woods can be carried out by laminating.

DEFORMING PLASTICS

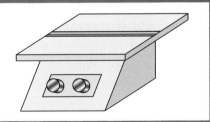

Strip heaters have an electrical element that provides heat to soften a line on a plastic sheet. When sufficiently softened the plastic can be bent or folded into the required shape.

BLOW MOULDING

Blow moulding is widely used for the mass production of plastic bottles and containers. Almost any shape of bottle can be produced as long as it does not have a handle. The containers can be transparent, opaque or coloured.

The first stage in the process is to clamp a parison (tube) of thermoplastic between the mould halves. Air is then blown into the mould.

This inflates the parison to take the shape of the mould. The product is then cooled and ejected automatically.

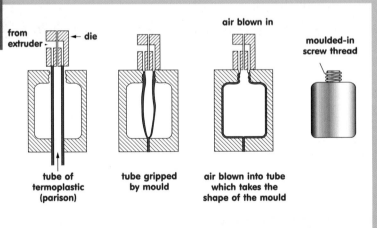

from extruder → die   air blown in

moulded-in screw thread

tube of termoplastic (parison)

tube gripped by mould

air blown into tube which takes the shape of the mould

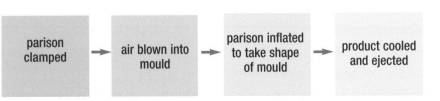

parison clamped → air blown into mould → parison inflated to take shape of mould → product cooled and ejected

Examiner's Top Tip
Know what products can be made by common deforming processes.

Note that line bending, vacuum forming and blow moulding are carried out on thermoplastics.

VACUUM FORMING

vacuum forming

Vacuum <u>forming</u> is a simple process that can be used to produce a <u>wide</u> <u>variety</u> <u>of</u> <u>products</u>. In industry these include <u>disposable</u> <u>drinking</u> <u>cups</u>, <u>margarine</u> <u>tubs</u>, <u>meat</u> <u>trays</u>, <u>egg</u> <u>cartons</u>, <u>picnic</u> <u>plates</u> and <u>baths</u>. In vacuum

air sucked out

forming the thermoplastic sheet is forced around a mould by <u>air</u> <u>pressure</u>. The sheet is <u>firstly</u> <u>heated</u> to make it pliable. <u>Moulds</u> can be made from <u>wood</u>, <u>metal</u>, <u>plastics</u> or <u>plaster</u>.
Vacuum forming is used widely in schools.

DEFORMING METALS

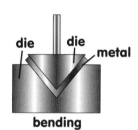
die   die
metal
bending

<u>Sheet</u> <u>metals</u> <u>and</u> <u>pipes</u> can be bent to shape using <u>formers</u> <u>and</u> <u>bending</u> <u>machines</u>. The metal may have to be <u>annealed</u> before the bending operation to soften it. When <u>accurate</u> <u>work</u> is required a <u>bending</u> <u>allowance</u> is made to allow for the <u>shortening</u> <u>effect</u> due to bending.

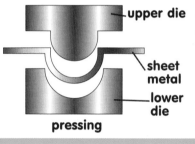
upper die
sheet metal
lower die
pressing

<u>Pressing</u> on to a <u>former</u> is a method used to make a wide range of <u>sheet</u> <u>steel</u> <u>products</u>. These include <u>car</u> <u>body</u> <u>parts</u> and the sides of <u>kitchen</u> <u>products</u> such as <u>fridges</u> <u>and</u> <u>washing</u> <u>machines</u>. Pressing is an accurate way of producing parts quickly.
Pressed-out sections are <u>less</u> <u>flimsy</u> than the original sheets due to the curves and creases that are pressed into the metal.
<u>Strengthening</u> <u>ribs</u> are often added to the shape.

LAMINATING AND DEFORMING WOODS

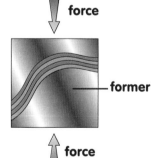
force
former
force

<u>Wood</u> can be deformed after <u>lamination</u> where <u>strips</u> <u>of</u> <u>wood</u> are glued together and then bent using <u>formers</u>. <u>Pressure</u> is first applied so that the layers are <u>well</u> <u>bonded</u> <u>together</u>.
Once a former has been made it can be used over again.
<u>Lamination</u> is used in structural applications such as <u>beams</u> and <u>arches</u> and in the construction of curved parts of <u>furniture</u>.

QUICK TEST

1. What is meant by the term deforming?
2. What types of product is vacuum forming used for?
3. What process is widely used for making plastic bottles?
4. What class of plastics is vacuum forming used for?
5. Name a method for deforming metals.
6. What is laminating?

6. Where strips of wood are glued and pressed together before forming.
5. Bending, pressing.
4. Thermoplastics.
3. Blow moulding.
2. Disposable drinking cups, margarine tubs, meat trays, egg cartons, picnic plates, baths.
1. Bringing about a change of shape without material loss.

PERMANENT JOINTING OF METALS AND PLASTICS

Examiner's Top Tip
Know which permanent joining processes are used for which material.

GOOD JOINTING METHODS

Permanent _fixings_ **cannot be** _taken_ _apart_.
Soldering, _welding_ **and** _riveting_ **are common permanent jointing methods for** _metals_.
Plastics **can be permanently joined using** _adhesives_ **and** _hot-air_ _welding_.
Good _joint_ _preparation_ **is essential in all cases to ensure that joints are of a** _high quality_.

METALS

SOFT SOLDERING

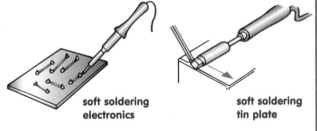

soft soldering electronics

soft soldering tin plate

Soldering is used to make joints of _medium strength_. It is usually used for making joints for copper and brass. Soldering is also used for making connections in _electrical_ and _electronic_ _circuits_.
Solder has a _low_ _melting_ _point_ and _must_ _not_ _be_ _used_ on joints that have to withstand too much _heat_.

TYPES OF SOLDER

Soft _solders_ are an alloy of tin and lead:

Tin content	Lead content	Uses
65%	35%	electrical solder
50%	50%	tinman's solder for general work
30%	70%	plumber's solder for plumbing joints

The joint to be soldered must be _cleaned_ with a file or emery cloth. For tinman's or plumber's solder a _flux_ is applied around the joint to _prevent_ _oxidation_. The joint is heated using a _soldering iron_ and the solder applied to the joint.
Electrical _solder_ has _flux_ embedded in its core.

RIVETS

Rivets **are used to join a wide variety of** _metals_ **and** _plastics_. **When riveting plastics care must be taken not to crack the plastic if it is brittle. Most rivets are made from** _steel_, _aluminium_ **or** _brass_.

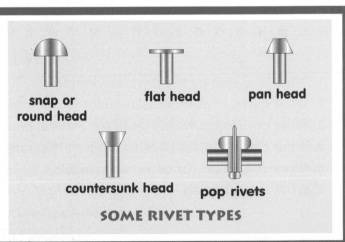

snap or round head

flat head

pan head

countersunk head

pop rivets

SOME RIVET TYPES

BRAZING AND SILVER SOLDERING

hard soldering

Brazing and <u>silver soldering</u> are termed <u>hard soldering</u>. They are used to produce <u>stronger joints</u> than those that can be achieved by soft soldering. <u>Hard solders</u> are <u>alloys of copper</u> and <u>zinc</u> in the form of a <u>brazing rod</u>. When <u>silver</u> is added they are called <u>silver solders</u>. In the same way as soft soldering the joint must be <u>thoroughly cleaned</u> and <u>flux</u> applied. The joint is heated to a <u>cherry red</u> using a <u>brazing torch</u>. The <u>brazing rod</u> is used to build up the joint.

In <u>soldering</u> and <u>brazing</u> the metal to be joined is not melted during the operation. The <u>solder</u> or <u>brazing rod</u> melts and flows into the capillaries of the metal joint and acts like a 'metallic glue' on cooling. In the case of <u>welding</u> the metal around the joint is melted and the melted <u>welding rod</u> helps to build up the joint.

WELDING

<u>Welding</u> is used where <u>high-strength joints</u> are required. <u>Oxyacetylene welding</u> uses an oxygen and acetylene gas to produce an <u>extremely hot flame</u>. <u>Electric arc welding</u> uses a high electrical current through a <u>welding electrode</u> to carry out the welding process. <u>Arc welding</u> is a quick and effective method of forming joints in <u>steel structures</u> and large assemblies.

When welding, a selection of joints are used to help strengthen the joint.

 fillet   **single butt**   **single vee butt**   **double vee butt**

JOINTING OF PLASTICS

 lapjoint

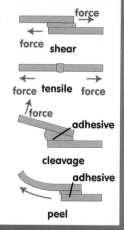
force
force **shear**
force **tensile** force
force
adhesive
cleavage
adhesive
peel

<u>Permanent jointing</u> can be achieved by using <u>adhesives</u> or <u>hot-air welding</u>.

When using adhesives the <u>appropriate type</u> must be used. For example, Tensol 12 is a <u>solvent-based adhesive</u> that is widely used for bonding <u>acrylics</u>. <u>Butt joints</u> can help to increase the <u>bonding area</u>.

The adhesive should be able to resist shear, tensile, cleavage and peel type forces.

A <u>hot-air gun</u> and <u>filler rod</u> can be used in <u>plastics welding</u>. The hot air has a high enough temperature to soften the material. The joints can be prepared in the same way as for metal welding.

QUICK TEST

1. State three methods of permanently joining metals.
2. State two methods of permanently joining plastics.
3. Which metals make up soft solder?
4. What is a flux used for?
5. Name two types of rivet.

5. Round, countersunk, flat, pan, pop.
4. To prevent oxidation when joints are heated.
3. Tin and lead.
2. Adhesives, hot-air welding.
1. Soft soldering, brazing, silver soldering, welding, riveting, adhesives.

PERMANENT JOINTING OF WOOD

TYPES OF WOOD JOINT

Wood joints are used in a wide range of applications from furniture to picture frames.

Traditional joints such as housing joints, mortise and tenons and dovetails are used with natural timbers.

Knock-down fittings tend to be used for joining man-made boards.

Joints in natural timber products are used for strength purposes and to enhance the appearance of the product.

DOWELS

Dowels can be used to reinforce simple butt joints. A PVA adhesive can be used to secure the dowels in the wood. Two dowels are generally used per joint. The holes can be drilled accurately with the aid of a drilling jig.

BUTT JOINTS

Butt joints are the simplest form of joint. They tend to be used for making frames. Corner pieces or metal staples can be used to strengthen up the joint.

MITRE JOINTS

Mitre joints are used to produce the corners of picture frames and other low-strength box frames. The mitre needs to be accurately cut to an angle of 45 degrees for right-angled corners. A jig can be used to help achieve this.

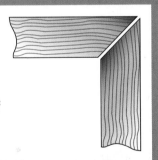

HOUSING JOINTS

Housing joints are often used in shelving constructions. A through housing is where the housing goes along the whole length of the side panel. A stopped housing only goes part of the way.

Stopped housing

Through housing

COMB OR FINGER JOINTS

These are <u>simple</u> <u>joints</u> that are used for <u>low-strength</u> <u>applications</u>. They are often used for making the <u>sides</u> <u>of</u> <u>boxes</u>.

DOVETAIL JOINTS

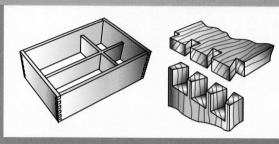

<u>Dovetails</u> provide <u>strong</u> <u>and</u> <u>decorative</u> <u>joints</u> for <u>furniture</u> and other applications. They are more difficult to make than finger joints.

MORTISE AND TENON JOINTS

<u>Mortise</u> <u>and</u> <u>tenon</u> <u>joints</u> are <u>strong</u> <u>joints</u> used in many constructions. The joints are made with the aid of a <u>tenon</u> <u>saw</u> to cut the tenons and a <u>mortise</u> <u>chisel</u> to cut out the mortises. They are used in <u>high-strength</u> <u>frame</u> constructions.

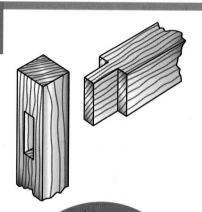

Examiner's Top Tip
Be able to draw clear diagrams of joints as part of designs.

QUICK TEST

1. Why are traditional joints used to join natural timbers?
2. What types of joints are commonly used for man-made timbers?
3. How can dowels be used for joints?
4. What angle is a right-angled mitre joint cut at?
5. What type of joints are commonly used for shelving?

1. To strengthen construction and enhance the appearance of the product.
2. Knock-down fittings.
3. To strengthen butt joints.
4. 45 degrees.
5. Housing joints.

TEMPORARY FASTENING METHODS

TYPES OF TEMPORARY FASTENERS

Temporary fasteners are used where the product may have to be assembled and dismantled regularly.
This is usually for inspection, maintenance or repair.
Temporary fasteners include nuts and bolts, socket screws and self-tapping screws.

Examiner's Top Tip
Fastenings are widely used in products. Be able to make clear sketches of the types used in your designs.

STUDS, SCREWS AND BOLTS

A nut and bolt can be used to hold parts together.
Studs are used where a joint is frequently dismantled.
The stud holds firmly whilst the nut can be undone.

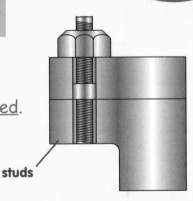

studs

caphead screw

Caphead socket screws or bolts are more expensive than hexagonal head bolts. They are made from high tensile steel which makes them very strong. They are usually screwed in and out using Allen keys. Caphead screws are widely used in the manufacture of machine tools and other equipment.

Cheesehead screws are used for applications such as cable clamping.

LOCKING DEVICES

Locking devices are used to prevent nuts from working loose due to vibration or other effects. Locking devices can either be positive or frictional. Positive locking is where the nuts are secured to the bolt with the aid of pins or plates. Examples of frictional locking devices and spring washers.

POSITIVE LOCKING DEVICES

- *hexagonal nut drilled for a split pin to hold the nut and bolt together*
- *castled nut with split pin*
- *tab washer*
- *hexagonal nut and plate*

FRICTIONAL DEVICES

- *locknuts*
- *nylon inserts in nut*
- *spring washer*

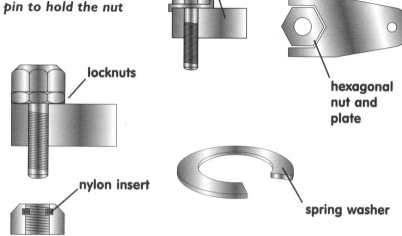

tab washer

locknuts

nylon insert

hexagonal nut and plate

spring washer

SELF-TAPPING SCREWS

Self-tapping screws can be used with plastic sheets and sheet metals. As their name suggests, they cut their own thread when being screwed into the material. A small hole is normally drilled first.

self-tapping screws

CLIPS

Clips are used with small screws to hold parts and components in place.

clip

self-tapping screw

WOOD SCREWS

round-head wood screw

countersunk wood screw

KNOCK-DOWN FITTINGS

TYPES OF KD FITTINGS

Knock-down (KD) fittings are used widely in the construction of flat-pack furniture.
Knock-down fittings can be use for school-based products especially when manufactured boards are being used.
The fittings allow furniture to be taken apart and re-assembled.
The main types of knock-down fittings are scan fittings, block-joint fittings, modesty blocks and disc and pegs.
Other fittings such as plates allow legs and other parts to be fastened to the products.

SCAN FITTINGS

Scan fittings are used for joining frame parts together, e.g. joining legs to table tops. A short length of aluminium bar with

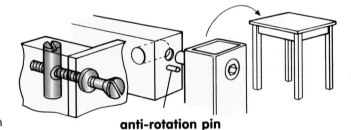

anti-rotation pin

a threaded hole is inserted into a hole in one section of the joint. A countersunk socket-head screw passes through the adjacent piece and is tightened to clamp the joint together. Dowels are often used to prevent any rotation of the two pieces of wood.

DISC AND PEGS

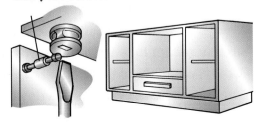

this part screws in

Disc and pegs are a variation of the scan fitting method. The disc can be pressed into the location hole. A screwdriver is used to align the disc so that its hole can align with and clamp the peg.

BLOC-FITTING

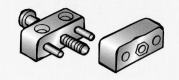
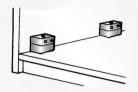

These are used for <u>butt-jointing</u> <u>corners</u> and <u>tee</u> <u>joints</u> for shelving. A bloc-fitting has two pieces which screw together to make a 90 degree angle. The fitting has one half screwed to each piece of board and the halves are fixed together using the screw provided with the joint. These types of joints can be very quickly dismantled.

MODESTY BLOC

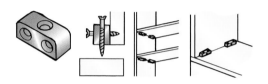

A <u>modesty</u> <u>bloc</u> has three screws to join the parts together. Two screws fit into one of the pieces, the other screw fits into the other piece. They are used for light constructions and for fixing shelves.

PLATE FIXINGS

<u>Plate</u> <u>fixings</u> are widely used for <u>securing</u> <u>legs</u> <u>to</u> <u>tables</u> where the joints have to be <u>taken</u> <u>apart</u> 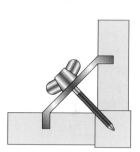 <u>regularly</u>. Some use <u>wing</u> <u>nuts</u> so that the joints can be disassembled quickly.

HINGES

<u>Cabinet</u> <u>hinges</u> are used for <u>kitchen</u> <u>and</u> <u>bedroom</u> <u>furniture</u> <u>doors</u>. They have small adjustment screws to align the door. 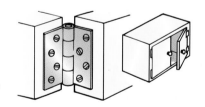 When fitting, care must be taken to mark the position of the blocks so that the parts fit together accurately. Small pilot holes can be drilled into manufactured board so that screws drive into the wood easily. Twin fast screws should be used.

Examiner's Top Tip
Use knock-down fittings if designs use man-made boards.

QUICK TEST

1. Why are knock-down fittings used for furniture?
2. Name two types of knock-down fittings.
3. For what are plate fittings used on furniture?
4. What measure can be taken to help start screws in man-made boards?

4. Drill a pilot hole.
3. Screwing on legs to main frame.
2. Scan fittings, disc and peg, block fitting, modesty block fitting, plate fittings, hinges.
1. So that they can be stored and delivered as flatpacks, allow furniture to be taken apart and re-assembled.

CHOOSING THE RIGHT FITTINGS

The proper assembly of parts is essential to make sure that they are secure and fit together correctly.
In the case of metals and plastics this can involve drilling and tapping holes, filing parts to make them fit, brazing and bolting parts together.
For wood this may involve the assembly of carcase, stool frame and flat-frame constructions.
Care must be taken not to overtighten nuts and bolts, to ensure that the correct size of screws are used and that work is checked for squareness and flatness.

TYPES OF WOOD CONSTRUCTION

CARCASE CONSTRUCTIONS

These are where sheets or planks of wood are joined to make box-type shapes. They are used for making bookshelves, cabinets, cupboards and drawers. Carcases need to be cramped in two directions at once so that the whole structure can be pulled together.

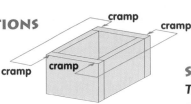

cramp cramp cramp cramp

STOOL FRAMES

These are used for the supporting structure for chairs, tables and similar products. The shorter sides are assembled first. When the glue has dried the other parts are assembled and the cramps placed across the larger sides.

cramp cramp cramp cramp

FLAT FRAMES

These are used to make flat shapes. Examples are doors, window frames and picture frames. Cramps are placed across the shorter rails of the frame and are along their centre lines.

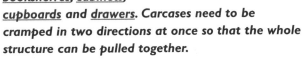

cramp cramp cramp cramp

Sash cramps and G-cramps are used to cramp wooden constructions together whilst they are gluing.

G-cramps

sash cramps

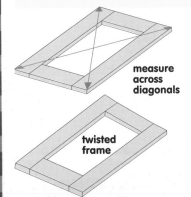

measure across diagonals

twisted frame

When cramping the squareness of the construction should be checked with the aid of a try square and by measuring across the diagonals. If the diagonal measurements are not the same it means that the frame is out of square. The frames and cramps can be adjusted to make the frame square.

Twisting (winding) should be checked to make sure that the frames are flat. This can be done by ensuring that the whole of the underside or topside of the frame will sit on a flat surface.

Examiner's Top Tip
Know the main types of constructions for wood.

CUTTING THREADS

Because dies are adjustable and taps are not, the internal thread is cut first. A cutting paste is used to aid the cutting operation. For the external threads the dies are opened to their maximum size by adjusting the screws in the die stock. After cutting the thread it can be tested in the tapped hole. If the thread is too tight the die-stock screws can be adjusted to reduce the diameter of the die. A second cut can then be taken.

TIPS FOR CRAMPING

Examiner's Top Tip
Know the difference between clearance and tapping holes and indicate them on your designs.

- Assemble job without glue first to ensure that the parts fit together.
- Assemble in easy stages.
- Do not use too much glue which will spoil the finish of the product.
- Wipe excess glue off the job before it dries.

Nails and screws are used for some jointing methods.
When using nails, nail though the thinner piece of wood into the thicker piece. The length of the nail should be about three times as long as the thinner piece of wood.
When using screws with hardwood or manufactured boards drill a pilot hole first. A clearance hole should be used for the shank of the screw. Screws can be lubricated using wax if necessary.

A bradawl can be used to help start screws in softwoods.
Screw caps and screw cups can be used to improve the appearance of assembled products.

bradawl

ASSEMBLY AND FITTING

METALS AND PLASTICS

Assembling and fitting is generally achieved by cross-filing, draw-filing and finishing off with emery cloth. Try squares and rules are used to check for squareness and flatness. When using a rule, one way to minimise errors is to use a lathe tool bit as a datum face.

When machine screws or bolts are used to clamp two pieces together, a clearance hole is needed for the hole in one side of the component whilst a tapping drill hole is required in the other side. Where possible, both pieces should be clamped together and the holes marked out on one of the pieces. Tool makers' clamps may be used for this purpose.

scrap wood

drill table

Both holes are then drilled with the tapping drill and then taken apart. The clearance hole can then be enlarged using the correct drill size.

QUICK TEST

1. Name two types of wood constructions.
2. How can a frame be tested for squareness?
3. What sort of hole is used for the shank of a screw to go through?
4. Why is the external thread cut after an internal one when using a tap and die?
5. What tool can be used to help start screws in soft woods?

1. Carcase, stool, flat.
2. By measuring across the diagonals.
3. Clearance hole.
4. Because the die can be adjusted.
5. Bradawl.

FINISHING PROCESSES FOR WOOD

Timber products require finishing treatments to protect them from the weather, insect and fungal attack, liquids and dirt.
Some hardwoods, for example, teak and iroko, have natural protection from their own oils and therefore do not always need protecting using a finishing treatment. Timber used for outdoor work and structural applications require treatment with preservatives.
Wood products such as furniture, children's toys and indoor shelving require varnishing, waxing, staining or painting.

CLEANING BEFORE FINISHING

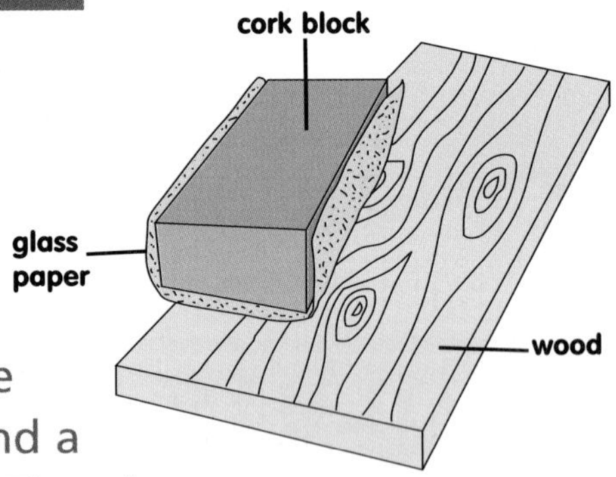

Scrapers are used to produce a very smooth finish on hardwoods after using a smoothing plane. Cabinet scrapers hold the blade firmly in a cast-iron body and are used to produce a high-class finish on furniture and other products.

Glass paper removes scratches and other flaws on the surface. Glass paper should be wrapped tightly around a cork sanding block to prevent damage to the wood. The glass grit size varies from coarse, medium, fine and extra-fine. Sanding is carried out firstly with a coarser grit paper and then progressively working down to a finer grit paper.

cork block
glass paper
wood

WOOD PRESERVES

Many wood preservers have to be handled with care because they are poisonous. Gloves should be worn.

Preservers can be applied by:
- *Brushing – gives a coating on the surface of the wood.*
- *Spraying – a quicker way of giving a surface finish.*
- *Soaking in tanks – gives better penetration and better protection.*
- *Forcing under pressure – specialised equipment is used to give the best protection.*

A common preservative is creosote. This is a type of tar oil which is used for outdoor applications such as fences and sheds.

CLEANING BEFORE FINISHING

FRENCH POLISH

This is available in a range of <u>colours</u>. The first coat of polish is applied with a brush to <u>seal the grain</u>. The polish is applied with long strokes <u>along the grain</u> and allowed to dry.

WAX POLISH

This produces a dull <u>gloss</u> <u>finish</u> and shows the natural grain of the wood. The wood is firstly <u>sealed</u> and then the wax is rubbed into the grain using soft cloth. Once dry the surface of the wood can be polished with a soft cloth.

POLYURETHANE VARNISH

This produces a <u>gloss</u> <u>finish</u> or <u>matt</u> <u>finish</u> depending on the product used. It is <u>heat-proof</u> and can take knocks well and can resist most liquids. The varnish is applied with a brush or cloth and lightly rubbed with fine glass paper in between coats.

OILS

These are used to produce a <u>natural</u> <u>finish</u> in timbers. They are suitable for indoor and outdoor use. Examples include <u>teak</u> <u>oil</u>, <u>olive</u> <u>oil</u> and <u>linseed</u> <u>oil</u>. The oil is worked well into the wood using a cloth. Any excess is wiped off after it has soaked into the wood.

STAINS

These can be used to give the appearance of other woods. They are also used to <u>colour the wood</u>. Stain can be brushed on or applied using a cloth.

PAINT

Paint is graded for either <u>inside use</u> or <u>outside use</u>. A <u>paint primer</u> should be used first to help <u>seal the wood</u>. Paint surfaces need to be clean and dry and the surfaces can be lightly sanded with glass paper before and between coats. An <u>undercoat</u> is applied after the primer and this is followed by one or more paint layers, finishing with a <u>top coat</u>.

Examiner's Top Tip
Know the different ways of applying different wood finishes.

QUICK TEST

1. Why do timbers need protecting?
2. What are the four general grades of glasspaper?
3. How should wax polish be applied to wood?
4. Name a timber that has a natural oil protection?
5. Name two ways that wood preservers can be applied to timbers.

5. Brushing, spraying, soaking in tanks, using pressure.
4. Teak, iroko.
3. Rubbed into the grain with a soft cloth.
2. Coarse, medium, fine, extra-fine.
1. To protect against weather, insects, fungal attack, liquids and dirt.

FINISHING PROCESSES FOR METALS AND PLASTICS

TYPES OF FINISH

Finishing processes are used to give the product a good appearance, protection against corrosion and to give the material a good surface finish.
Files and emery cloths can be used to remove flaws and marks made by hand and machine processes.
Oils, paints, lacquer and plastic coatings can be used to give metals a protective finish.
Industrial products are often chrome- or tin-plated.
Enamelling can be used to give a decorative finish to sheet metals and copper or brass jewellery.

FINISHING

High quality finishes can be achieved on plastics by filing and rubbing down with wet and dry paper. Metal polish can be used to clean up the edge. Sides and faces can be polished using a buffing machine.

ELECTROPLATING

Electroplating is used in industry to chrome- and tin-plate products.
Electroplating give a decorative finish as well as protecting the metal against corrosion. It is used for a range of products from car bumpers to furniture and kitchenware.

DRAW FILING

Draw-filing is used to clean up the edges of plastics or the faces of metals. During draw-filing the file is moved sideways along the work to obtain a smooth finish after cross-filing.

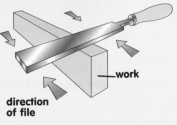

direction of file

work

FINISHING BRIGHT MILD STEEL

The work is cleaned by draw-filing so that marks are removed from the surface of the work. The work should be filed in the same direction. Chalk can be rubbed into the file to give a smoother finish. The work can then be finished using different grades of emery cloth. The cloth is wrapped across the face of a flat file and worked in the same direction as the draw-filing marks. To protect from rusting the work can be smeared with a thin layer of grease or oil.

CELLULOSE PAINTS

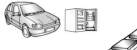

The surface needs to be <u>thoroughly</u> <u>cleaned</u> and <u>degreased</u> using <u>paraffin</u> or <u>cleaning</u> <u>solvents</u>. <u>Care</u> <u>must</u> <u>be</u> <u>taken</u> when doing this. A <u>primer</u> and <u>undercoat</u> should be applied before the <u>top</u> <u>coat</u> layers. The paint layers can be applied by <u>spraying</u> or by using a <u>brush</u>. Spraying must be carried out in a <u>well-ventilated</u> room or in a spray booth with <u>extraction</u> <u>facilities</u>. Care should be taken to prevent the <u>paints</u> <u>running</u> and the work can be lightly <u>rubbed</u> <u>down</u> with emery cloth in between layers.

PLASTIC COATINGS

<u>Plastic</u> <u>coatings</u> can be achieved using a <u>fluidised</u> <u>bed</u>. Plastic coating (<u>dip</u> <u>coating</u>) is used to coat products such as vegetable racks, wire baskets and metal furniture. The metal needs to be <u>cleaned</u> and <u>de-greased</u>. It is then <u>heated</u>, usually in an oven, to a temperature of 180ºC. The product is then <u>dipped</u> into the plastic powder in a fluidised bed until the metal is <u>coated</u> with melted plastic. It is then removed and left to <u>cool</u> <u>and</u> <u>solidify</u>.

LACQUERS

These can be used on <u>non-ferrous</u> <u>metals</u> such as copper or brass to prevent the metal from <u>tarnishing</u>. They can be cleaned up using <u>wet</u> <u>and</u> <u>dry</u> <u>paper</u> and then polished up on a buffing machine. The lacquer can be applied with a soft brush. Lacquering gives a good <u>appearance</u> to the metal.

ENAMELLING

<u>Enamelling</u> can be used to produce designs and <u>patterns</u> <u>on</u> <u>jewellery</u>. It is also used on <u>cookers</u>, <u>washing</u> <u>machines</u>, <u>sinks</u> and <u>baths</u>. However plastics have taken over many of these applications.

QUICK TEST

1. What type of filing method is generally used to obtain a good finish on metals and plastics?
2. What preparations should be carried out before applying cellulose paints?
3. Name a product that is plastic-coated.
4. Name a finish that can be achieved using electroplating.
5. Why is lacquer often used as a finish for copper and brass?

Examiner's Top Tip
Be able to give finishes for common metal products.

1. Draw-filing.
2. Degrease and clean.
3. Vegetable racks, wire baskets, metal furniture.
4. Chrome-plating, tin-plating.
5. To stop it from tarnishing.

CNC IN MANUFACTURING

CNC APPLICATIONS

Examiner's Top Tip
Where possible incorporate CNC work into designs.

- CNC stands for <u>computer</u> <u>numerical</u> <u>control</u>.
- <u>CNC</u> <u>processes</u> are now <u>widely</u> <u>used</u> in the <u>school</u> <u>workshop</u> as well as industry.
- <u>CNC</u> <u>machines</u> include <u>engravers</u>, <u>routers</u>, <u>milling</u> <u>machines</u> and <u>lathes</u>.
- Some machines have milling and turning <u>functions</u> <u>combined</u>.
- CNC machines produce <u>high-quality</u> <u>finishes</u> and they can be <u>programmed</u> to machine <u>awkward</u> <u>and</u> <u>difficult</u> <u>shapes</u>.

PROGRAMMING

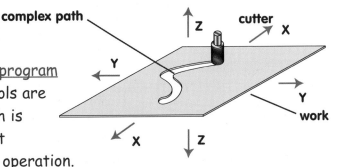

complex path   cutter

A <u>CNC</u> <u>machine</u> requires a <u>computer</u> <u>program</u> to operate it. Most machines in schools are linked up to a <u>central</u> <u>computer</u> which is usually <u>Windows-based</u>. This makes it easier to carry out the programming operation.
<u>Industrial</u> <u>machines</u>, however, may have a <u>special</u> <u>machine</u> <u>code</u> which makes them more <u>difficult</u> <u>to</u> <u>program</u>.
A program will typically contain <u>information</u> about the <u>X</u>, <u>Y</u> and <u>Z</u> co-ordinates required for the <u>cutting</u> <u>movements</u>. These include the <u>depth</u> <u>of</u> <u>cut</u> for each machining pass, the <u>operating</u> <u>speed</u> and <u>feed</u> <u>rate</u> of the cutters. The program also specifies which <u>type</u> <u>of</u> <u>cutter</u> to use.
Programs can be saved on <u>hard</u> <u>or</u> <u>floppy</u> <u>disks</u>. Some machines use <u>smart</u> <u>cards</u>.

SAFETY FIRST

<u>MDF</u> and other <u>manufactured</u> <u>boards</u> are commonly used on <u>CNC</u> <u>routing</u> <u>machines</u>. The dust from these materials is <u>hazardous</u> <u>if</u> <u>inhaled</u>. The <u>COSHH</u> (<u>Control</u> <u>of</u> <u>Substances</u> <u>Hazardous</u> <u>to</u> <u>Health</u>) Regulations require that there are good <u>dust</u> <u>extraction</u> facilities attached to the routing machines. As an extra precaution <u>dust</u> <u>masks</u> should be worn.

CNC SYSTEMS DIAGRAM

Systems diagrams are used widely in CNC technology to help break down a system into simpler parts. A systems diagram is shown right:

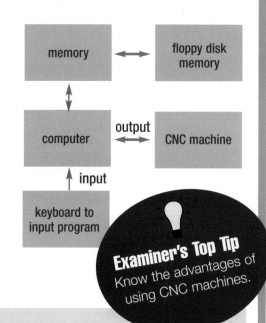

CNC ROUTING MACHINES

These are used widely in the school workshop for a range of wood-machining operations. Different sizes of routing tools can be used and the machine can route out complex shapes. School routers tend to be much smaller than those found in industry and the size of pieces that can be machined are relatively small. This can limit their use on some project work such as tables and cabinets.

Examiner's Top Tip
Know the advantages of using CNC machines.

CNC LATHES

These can carry out all the turning operations of a manual lathe. They machine at a much quicker rate and difficult operations like screw cutting and machining curved profiles are easily achieved. CNC lathes for schools are expensive pieces of machinery and also tend to be smaller than the manual lathes used. This can limit the size of job that can be carried out.

CNC MILLING MACHINES

These can cut complex curved paths and profiles very accurately. Some of these would be very difficult to achieve using manual milling methods. They can machine at fast rates and produce high-quality finishes. Few jigs and fixtures are required since the tool can move accurately to the positions required for milling, slotting and drilling. As with the CNC lathe they tend to be more expensive to buy than manual machines. However, the machining advantages can outweigh the cost.

CNC ENGRAVING MACHINES

These can engrave on thin pieces of material. They are often used for making signs and parts for the assembly of electronic components and other complex products. They can cut small complex shapes accurately. Engraving machines use small diameter cutters. These can easily break if the depth of cut is too much or the cutting speed and feed is too high. The appropriate cutting speeds should be programmed into the machine.

ADVANTAGES OF USING CNC MACHINES IN SCHOOL WORKSHOPS

- Produces accurate shapes.
- Can machine complex shapes which would be difficult to machine manually.
- Produces high-quality surface finishes.
- Can machine at a fast rate compared with manual methods.
- Can produce identical components quickly and easily.
- Requires few jigs and fixtures.

QUICK TEST

1. What does CNC stand for?
2. Give an example of CNC machines found in schools.
3. How can CNC programs be saved?
4. What are the advantages of using CNC machines in workshops?

1. Computer numerical control.
2. Lathes, milling machines, routers, engravers.
3. Hard disks, floppy disks, smart cards.
4. Can produce accurate shapes, machine-complex shapes, produce high- quality finishes, fast machining rate, no need for many jigs and fixtures.

TESTING FOR QUALITY

TOOLS FOR QUALITY CHECKS

<u>Quality</u> <u>checks</u> are made from time to time on manufactured components and products using <u>engineer's</u> <u>squares</u>, <u>callipers</u>, <u>micrometers</u> and <u>verniers</u>. This is called <u>quality</u> <u>control</u>. These tools should be <u>kept</u> <u>in</u> <u>good</u> <u>condition</u> so that they maintain their <u>accuracy</u>.

CARE

<u>Precision</u> <u>measuring</u> <u>tools</u> and <u>instruments</u> are made to <u>high</u> <u>quality</u> <u>standards</u>. In industry these tools are <u>periodically</u> <u>checked</u> to ensure that they <u>retain</u> <u>their</u> <u>accuracy</u>. <u>Measuring</u> <u>tools</u> should be <u>treated</u> <u>with</u> <u>care</u> to retain their <u>initial</u> <u>accuracy</u>. They should be kept clean and not dropped.

When making <u>quality</u> <u>checks</u>, care must be taken to wipe any dirt or grease off the components to be measured. Any <u>burrs</u> should be carefully removed using a file. Burrs can damage precision instruments and make the measurements and tests incorrect.

TRY SQUARES

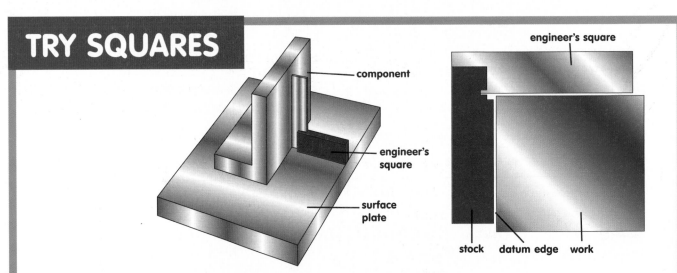

These are used to test whether <u>one surface is square to another</u>. To test, the work is held up to the light and the stock is placed against the datum face. If no light shows under the blade the second face is square. <u>Larger</u> <u>components</u> can be checked using an <u>engineer's</u> <u>square</u> and <u>surface</u> <u>plate</u>.

CALLIPERS

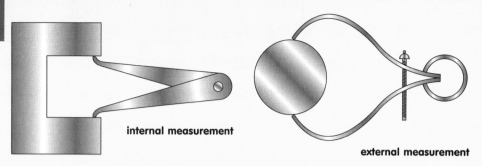

internal measurement

external measurement

These are used in conjunction with a rule to measure diameters. Firm-joint callipers are usually used for large sizes. Spring-joint callipers are used for more accurate work. They can be used to measure to an accuracy of 0.25 mm. The accuracy of a pair of callipers depends upon the 'feel' of the user. Both inside and outside diameters can be measured.

MICROMETERS

Micrometers can measure much more accurately than callipers. They can be used to measure to accuracies of 0.001 mm or less. External micrometers are used for measuring outside measurements. Internal micrometers are used for internal measurements. The most common external micrometer ranges from 0 to 25 mm. Digital micrometers provide a direct readout making it easier to read.

VERNIER CALLIPERS

These also make internal and external measurements. Larger measurements than a micrometer can be achieved. Verniers have typical accuracies of 0.02 mm.

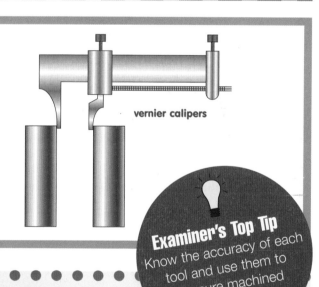

vernier calipers

Examiner's Top Tip
Know the accuracy of each tool and use them to measure machined components

QUICK TEST

1. What are callipers used for?
2. How are try squares used to check components?
3. What is the accuracy of a metric micrometer?
4. How should precision measuring tools be cared for?
5. What is the accuracy of vernier callipers?

5. 0.02 mm.
4. Kept clean and not dropped.
3. 0.001 mm.
2. Work is held up to the light and the stock placed against the datum face.
1. To measure outside or inside diameters.

EXAM QUESTIONS — Use the questions to test your progress. Check your answers on pages 94–95.

1. A plastic link is to be injection-moulded in a batch of 5000.

Complete the diagram showing the main stages of

injection moulding. (4 marks)

....

....

2. A securing bracket is to be made from sheet metal.

a) State a metal that could be used. (1 mark)

....

....

b) State an advantage of pressing the metal out of the sheet rather than using other processes. (1 mark)

....

....

3. For what purpose would you use a (i) bevel-edged chisel (ii) jack plane (iii) spoke-shave? (3 marks)

....

4. A 45 mm hole is to be drilled in a piece of plastics sheet.

a) Name a tool that could be used. (1 mark)

....

....

b) Explain why a pilot hole would be drilled before using the tool. (1 mark)

....

5. Before drilling a piece of steel a risk assessment should be carried out. Give two precautions you would

take before drilling. (2 marks)

....

....

6. Knock-down (KD) fittings are to be used to fit together a shelving unit. The fittings are to be compression

moulded.

a) Explain why they are called knock-down fittings. (1 mark)

....

....

b) Give two reasons why the manufacturer has chosen compression moulding rather than machining from a

solid block. (2 marks)

....

....

7. A small clamp is to be made in the workshop.

State three stages used to make the internal thread

after marking out. (3 marks)

....

internal thread

8. a) State one method that can be used to bend a plastic sheet. (1 marks)

....

b) Explain a method whereby wood can be permanently bent into shape. (1 mark)

....

....

9. What type of saw would you use to saw:

a) A piece of 22 mm x 42 mm softwood. (1 mark)

....

b) A piece of 10 mm square mild steel bar. (1 mark)

....

c) An irregular shape in polystyrene sheet. (1 mark)

....

10. How could a 15-mm piece of square section bar be held in centre lathe? (1 mark)

....

11. 100 aluminium feet are to be made in a workshop.

a) Name a suitable casting process that could be used. (1 mark)

....

....

b) State one reason why casting may be a better method to

make them rather than machining. (1 mark)

....

....

12. What heat-joining method can be used for (i) electrical joints (ii) joining together mild steel (iii) joining

together copper parts? (3 marks)

....

How did you do?

1–3	correct	....start again
4–6	correct	....getting there
7–9	correct	....good work
10–12	correct	....excellent

1. Two pieces of mild steel tube are to be joined together using a mitre angle.

Explain three stages you would use to mark out and cut the metal ready

for welding. (3 marks)

joint

....

....

2. a) Name a type of glue you would use for gluing up a softwood mitred frame. (1 mark)

....

....

b) State a test you could use to make sure that the frame was square. (1 mark)

....

....

3. The drawing shows the detail needed to be marked out on a piece of BDMS.

a) Name the tools you would use to mark out the lines,

punch the hole and mark out the radius. (3 marks)

....

....

b) Name two tools you would use to remove the waste. (2 marks)

....

....

4. A table is to be made from wood.

a) Name a suitable construction for the joint at point A. (1 mark)

....

....

b) State i) two tools used for marking out the joint

and ii) two tools used to cut the joint. (4 marks)

....

....

5. A small hook is to be made from plastic.

Name the equipment you would use for i) marking out ii)

sawing and iii) finishing. (3 marks)

....

....

6. a) What type of frictional locking device could be used to secure a nut onto a machine bolt? (1 mark)

....

....

b) State a type of permanent fixing method that could be used to join two pieces of brass together. (1 mark)

....

....

c) Give two precautions you would take to ensure a good joint. (2 marks)

....

....

7. A milk-bottle rack is to be made from 6 mm diameter BDMS bar which has been brazed together.

....

a) Describe a finish that could be used for the rack. (1 mark)

....

....

b) Describe how the wire could be prepared ready for finishing after brazing. (2 marks)

....

....

8. a) How can you avoid splitting wood when planning across the grain?

....

....

b) Describe the measures you would take to successfully screw two pieces of i) hardwood ii) softwood. (2 marks)

....

....

9. State how marks left from the filing of mild steel can be removed. (1 mark)

10. a) What are vee blocks and clamps used for? (1 mark)

....

b) What is the purpose of a surface plate and surface gauge? (1 mark)

....

How did you do?

1–2	correct	....start again
3–5	correct	....getting there
6–8	correct	....good work
9–10	correct	....excellent

TYPES OF PRODUCTION

Industrial production methods can be divided into one of four general categories: job, batch, in-line and continuous flow production. Each category depends largely upon the numbers of products that are being manufactured and by the type of equipment being used. Computer-controlled manufacturing systems are now widely used, especially in the fields of batch, in-line and continuous production.

JOB PRODUCTION

Job is used to manufacture one-offs or very small numbers. Examples include prototypes and tools for presswork equipment and assembly jigs. General-purpose machines such as lathes, milling machines and welding equipment are usually used. Machinery is not used on a continuous basis but only when required. Workers within this type of production need to be highly skilled in a range of areas and to able to work on a number of aspects of a project.

BATCH MANUFACTURE

Most industrial manufacture falls into this category. During batch production the operation is divided into a number of separate stages. A batch of sub-assemblies is made during each stage of the operation and the batches are advanced through the production system for completion. Individual components are added at appropriate stages. Batch sizes can vary from a few to ones numbering many thousands. It is much quicker to manufacture components using this method than trying to manufacture them one at a time. Jigs and fixtures are often used to speed up the process. Batch production is especially suited to computer-controlled manufacturing methods since the machines can be reprogrammed quickly for different batch sizes and batch types.

Examiner's Top Tip
Be familiar with the components or assemblies made in batch production.

IN-LINE PRODUCTION

In-line production is used mainly for mass production of products such as cars, washing machines and fridges. The products are assembled as they flow down a production line. Semi-skilled operators tend to be used in the process. In-line production plants are very expensive to set up and thousands of products have to be made and sold to offset the capital costs. Production is often difficult to plan and breakdowns are costly. Many lines or part lines are controlled by computers which can also monitor production.

CONTINUOUS PRODUCTION

Continuous production refers to processes such as oil refining and chemical processing. Once production has started the plants tend to run continuously and automatically. Start-up times tend to be long since the process has to be started gradually. Continuous production plants tend to have sophisticated computer systems to monitor how the product is flowing through the system, and measures temperatures, liquid levels and other quality control quantities.

FLEXIBILITY

Manufacturing flexibility refers to how quickly a machine or manufacturing system can be changed to make a different type or different number of components or assemblies. Machines used in batch production are usually selected because of their flexibility. CNC machines are flexible because they can be programmed quickly and easily when different batch types and sizes are required. This is termed quick response. In-line and continuous production plants are less flexible because it is far more difficult to change them for different product types.

QUICK TEST

1. What is job production?
2. What attachments can be used to help speed up batch production processes?
3. What sort of products are made by in-line production?
4. What sorts of products are manufactured by continuous production plants?
5. What is meant by manufacturing flexibility?

5. How quickly a machine can be changed to make a different type or number of components.
4. Oil, chemicals.
3. Cars, washing machines, fridges.
2. Jigs and fixtures.
1. Where one-off or a small number of components are made.

79

COMMERCIAL SYSTEMS

Manufacturing industry makes use of a range of business systems to help make them more efficient and to produce quality products. Common systems are production cells, concurrent manufacture, total quality management and just-in-time methods.

PRODUCTION CELLS

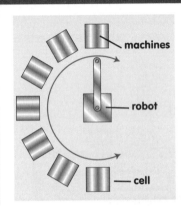

machines

robot

cell

A production cell is a group of machines or a group of people and machines that work together to produce components or products. In the car industry, for example, robot cells are used to assemble, weld, spray and finish parts such as car door panels and floor panels. Other cells consist of people working as a team. Each person is not dedicated to a particular machine or role but will swap and change according to the tasks to be carried out. Team-working cells are widely used during batch production when a quick response to orders is required. Here the team will have responsibility for planning how the different batches will be made, decide which machines will be used and who will operate them and also be responsible for the quality control of the product.

CONCURRENT MANUFACTURE

Concurrent engineering is used to reduce the time it takes between the design stage and the manufacture of a product.

Examiner's Top Tip
Relate industrial processes to your own project designs.

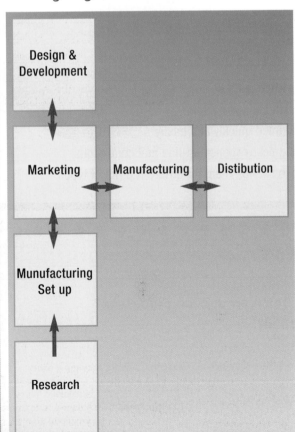

Design & Development

Marketing

Manufacturing

Distibution

Munufacturing Set up

Research

In the traditional approach of manufacturing the tasks would have been completed in separate stages. This means that product design is carried out in the design department. The designs are then passed onto the production planning department for further work. Once completed, prototypes are made in the modelling shop and tested in the research and development department. Then manufacturing and finishing can commence. Finally the product can be field-tested and distributed. This approach is very time-consuming and leads to long lead times between the design stages and manufacture. In addition, potential manufacturing problems will not be identified until the manufacturing stage. Often these problems have to 'go back to the drawing board'.

In concurrent manufacturing, however, all departments are involved at the design stage and aspects of testing and manufacturing can be analysed prior to production starting. This cuts down the lead time between the design stage and full scale manufacture. It also reduces the risk of producing designs that cannot be manufactured properly or might fail in the field.

JUST-IN-TIME MANUFACTURING

Just-in-time manufacturing is used to reduce the stocks of goods that build up during manufacture. It also helps to ensure that companies are not left with too many unsold goods at the end of a production run. Just-in-time ensures that the minimum quantities of components are purchased and delivered and assembled at the right time with minimum waste.

Advantages of just-in-time	Disadvantages of just-in-time
Reduces stock piles in factory	Possibility of products not reaching production stages on time
Reduces stock holding costs	Reliant on the quality standards of suppliers
Eliminates unsold goods at end of production run	Reduces choice of suppliers
Improves factory housekeeping	
Helps to strengthen relationships with suppliers	
Makes use of standard components, thus keeping costs down	
Demands tighter quality control	

ELECTRONIC POINT OF SALE SYSTEM

The EPOS systems that are used in supermarkets and shops are good examples of how just-in-time works in practice. When a purchase is made the barcode reading system records that the stock level is lowered. This information is automatically computed and sent back to suppliers or warehouses over telecom links. The stock can then be topped up hourly or daily as required and always 'just in time'.

TOTAL QUALITY MANAGEMENT (TQM)

Total quality management emphasises the importance of product, process and procedure quality at every stage of management and manufacture. TQM does not rely solely on quality inspections at the end of the process. Total quality management relies on everyone in the factory being responsible for their own quality standards. Quality checks can be made at each stage of manufacture. If there are any problems these can be sorted out there and then. This helps to ensure that faults are found at early stages and not at the end of the manufacturing process. TQM helps reduce the number of rejected components.

QUICK TEST

1. What is a production cell?
2. Why is concurrent manufacturing used?
3. Give three advantages of just-in-time.
4. What is meant by EPOS?
5. What is meant by TQM?
6. Why is TQM important?

6. All workers are responsible for quality and quality checks are made at all stages of management and production.
5. Total quality management.
4. Electronic point of sale.
3. Reduction of stock piles, reduces stock holding costs, eliminates unsold goods.
2. To reduce the lead time between design and manufacture.
1. A group of machines or a group of people and machines working together to produce components.

BATCH PRODUCTION

Most products are manufactured using <u>batch</u> <u>production</u> <u>methods</u>**.** <u>Batch</u> <u>production</u> **involves producing a** <u>specified</u> <u>number</u> <u>of</u> <u>identical</u> <u>products</u> **in groups. The product to be made is usually broken down into a number of** <u>components</u> **or** <u>sub-assemblies</u> **which are then made in batches.** <u>Batch production</u> **needs to be** <u>well</u> <u>planned</u>**.** <u>Computer-aided</u> <u>manufacturing</u> <u>methods</u> **and** <u>jigs</u> <u>and</u> <u>fixtures</u> **are widely used to speed up the production process.**

JIGS AND FIXTURES

When a number of identical components are to be made as a batch it is very <u>time-consuming</u> to measure and mark off each component individually before they are manufactured. <u>Jigs</u> <u>and</u> <u>fixtures</u> are used to <u>speed</u> <u>up</u> <u>the</u> <u>production</u> <u>process</u>. Jigs and fixtures are used to locate the workpiece quickly and clamp it into place so that measuring and marking out does not need to be carried out.

A <u>jig</u> is a device which <u>locates</u> <u>and</u> <u>holds</u> the work in place and also <u>guides</u> <u>the</u> <u>tool</u> for machining. This allows parts to be made accurately and quickly. Jigs used for <u>drilling</u> <u>or</u> <u>reaming</u> have hardened steel bushes to guide the tools.

As its name suggests, a <u>fixture</u> is a <u>work-holding</u> <u>device</u> that is <u>clamped</u> <u>to</u> <u>the</u> <u>table</u>. Fixtures can be used for operations such as <u>milling</u>, <u>grinding</u> <u>and</u> <u>turning</u>. Fixtures can also be used for <u>welding</u> <u>and</u> <u>assembly</u> work.

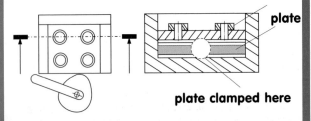

hardened steel bush

plate

plate clamped here

CLAMPING

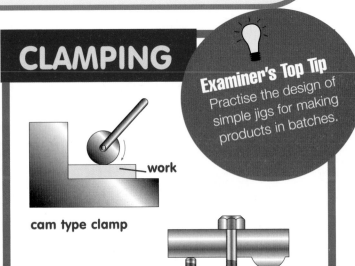

cam type clamp

←work

bridge type clamp

Clamps for jigs and fixtures need to release and tighten up quickly. Two types that are often used are bridge clamps and cam type clamps.

Examiner's Top Tip
Practise the design of simple jigs for making products in batches.

JIG & FIXTURE DESIGN

Jigs and fixtures need:

• a method of quickly locating the component
• to be foolproof so that the component can be only located the correct way round
• a method of positioning the tools accurately
• to allow guards to be used properly
• to allow swarf, wood or plastics cuttings to be cleaned quickly after each operation
• to allow the component to seat properly in the jig or fixture.

COMPUTER-AIDED MANUFACTURE

Computer-aided manufacturing is used widely in batch production processes. The way in which computer-aided machines can clamp and machine components has largely replaced the need for jigs and fixtures in many applications. The machines can be programmed easily for a particular batch of products. Computer control allows identical products to be made quickly and to a high degree of accuracy. Programs often allow complex shapes to be machined. The tools on computer machines are often changed automatically.

COSTING

Manufacturing costs can be broken down into direct and indirect costs.
Direct costs depend upon how many components are made in the batch.
They include the cost of labour and the cost of materials and the cost of other supplies.
Indirect costs include the costs of heating and lighting, wages for office staff, rents, rates and the cost of sales and marketing. Indirect costs do not generally change with the number of components being manufactured in the batch.
Computer-aided machines may be more expensive to buy in the first place. However, once programmed the direct costs can be lower due to minimal labour costs and wastage.

PRODUCTION COSTING
The cost of producing a batch of components is an important business factor.
In addition to the cost of buying the machine (capital cost) the following costs need to be calculated.

Computer machines	Machines using jigs and fixtures
Cost of initial programming	Cost of making jigs and fixtures
Material costs	Material costs
Overhead costs	Overhead costs
Supervisor costs	Operator costs
Running costs	Running costs
Cost of changing programs	Cost of setting up the machine

PLANNING
Planning is an essential business activity to ensure that batches are manufactured in the most appropriate sequence and on time to meet orders. Network charts can be used to help show the production route. Gantt charts can be used to indicate the sequence of operations and the time they will take.

QUICK TEST

1. What is meant by batch production?
2. What is meant by a jig?
3. What is meant by a fixture?
4. What type of tasks are carried using jigs?
5. What is meant by a direct cost?
6. Why are computer controlled machines used in batch production?

Examiner's Top Tip
Know the advantages of using jigs in batch production

1. Where a number of identical components are made in batches.
2. A device that locates and clamps the work and guides the tool.
3. A work-holding device which is clamped to the machine.
4. Drilling, reaming.
5. A cost that depends upon how many components are made.
6. Do not need jigs and fixtures, can make identical components quickly and easily.

USE OF STANDARD COMPONENTS

THE DEMAND FOR STANDARD COMPONENTS

There are very few designs that do not use standard components.

Examples where they are used are bicycles, cars, tumble driers and personal stereos.

Standard components include nuts, bolts, set screws, bearings, and bushes and gears.

Standard components are normally bought in to reduce costs.

Standard component suppliers form the backbone of parts of just-in-time systems.

WHY STANDARD COMPONENTS ARE USED

It is more expensive to make standard parts than to purchase them from a supplier.

The supplier may be making them in their thousands and therefore the cost of each component – the unit cost – will be kept low.

If the parts are made 'in house' special machines and tools have to bought. The unit cost will be high.

Many standard part manufacturers are specialists in their own field. They will have extensive experience in making reliable parts. This will ensure that good-quality components are bought in.

Standard component manufacturers often have good testing facilities to test for reliability and safety. This helps to make sure that the safety requirements have been met.

Suppliers' catalogues give the types and prices of parts that are available. In most cases the more that are bought the cheaper will be the unit price.

Many of the parts are manufactured to national standards, ensuring high quality and safety standards.

SOME NATIONAL STANDARDS

BS	British Standards
JIS	Japanese Industry Standards
ANSI	American National Standards Institute

INTERNATIONAL AND COMPANY STANDARDS

World trade has created the need for international standards. The International Standards Organisation has created a number of ISO standards for a wide range of products.

Many companies have their own systems for standardising components. These include design specifications and part numbering procedures.

STANDARD SIZES

Standard components are manufactured in a range of <u>standard</u> <u>sizes</u> and dimensions. <u>Metric</u> <u>coarse</u> <u>threads</u> for example have the range M2, M2.5, M3, M4, M5, M6, M8, M10 and M12 (where M2 refers to a 2 mm diameter thread).

In a similar way <u>bearings</u> have a range of standard inside and outside diameters.

Component sizes can be found in manufacturers' catalogues. The actual dimensions of a component can be used in the design of a product with confidence that it will fit.

Common standard components used in schools include <u>gears</u>, <u>bearings</u>, <u>pulleys</u>, <u>round</u> <u>bars</u> and <u>dowels</u> used for <u>shafts</u>, <u>nuts</u>, <u>bolts</u> and <u>wood</u> <u>screws</u>.

STANDARD PARTS AND JUST-IN-TIME MANUFACTURE

Standard parts' manufacturers make large numbers of just-in-time deliveries. When parts are required orders can be made using <u>computerised</u> <u>stock</u> <u>control</u> <u>systems</u> which speed up the <u>ordering</u> <u>process</u>. Standard components' manufacturers who supply companies on a just-in-time basis have to be well-organised.

QUICK TEST

1. Why do manufactures buy in standard components?
2. Name three standard components.
3. What does the term BS stand for?
4. Where can details and sizes of standard components be found?

1. Cheaper than making them in house
2. Nuts, bolts, set screws, bearings, bushes and gears
3. British Standard
4. Manufacturers' catalogues

USE OF CAD/CAM IN INDUSTRY

Computers are used widely in industry for both design and manufacturing operations. CAD refers to computer-aided design operations. CAM refers to computer-aided manufacturing operations. Computerisation allows designs to be easily downloaded to computer-controlled machinery. This can reduce the time between design and manufacture.

COMPUTER AIDED DESIGN

Computers are used in the design process in a number of ways. They are used to make accurate 2-D and 3-D drawings of components and products. Solid modelling is used to show how the product will look when made. Different colours and textures can be added to the model and the product can be rotated to show different views. Many CAD programs can determine how the product is likely to fail when in service using finite-element software packages.

Some CAD packages can be linked to rapid prototyping equipment. This builds up a 3-D wax or resin model of the product designed on the computer. Rapid prototyping equipment is expensive to buy. However, it allows a prototype to be made quickly without having to use expensive machinery and materials.

ADVANTAGES OF USING CAD PACKAGES

The design process can be speeded up.
Allows solid modelling of the product.
Enables design changes to be made quickly.
Information can be stored easily on disk.
Data can be easily transmitted to other design and manufacturing areas.

COMPUTER-AIDED MANUFACTURING

Computer-aided manufacturing (CAM) is used to describe the way in which components and products are made with the aid of computerised equipment. Computers allow new information to be programmed into the computer relatively easily and changes to be quickly carried out.

ADVANTAGES OF USING CAM

- Can be reprogrammed easily for different batch sizes.
- Can work continuously without the need to stop for breaks.
- Gives consistent quality levels.
- Can be used in hazardous conditions.
- Can be linked to computer-aided design facilities.
- Can be linked to a factory-wide computer system.

Examiner's Top Tip
Know the advantages and disadvantages of using CAD/CAM in industry.

CNC MACHINERY

Computer numerical control (CNC) machines form the most widely used class of computer-aided manufacturing equipment. A CNC machine uses a dedicated program which has been programmed into a process control unit. Machines can be programmed using special key pads, floppy discs or smart cards.

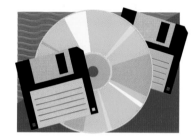

Industrial applications include CNC lathes, milling machines, routers, sheet metal presses, welding equipment and materials - handling equipment. CNC machining centres are machines which are able to be programmed to carry out a range of operations on the same machine such as turning, milling and drilling. On many CNC machines the tools can be changed automatically and measurements can be carried out automatically using sensor probes.

ROBOTS

Industrial robots are computer-controlled devices that can be programmed for many different operations. A robot can be reprogrammed with a new sequence of movements and can be easily adapted to new conditions. The original program need not be lost since it can be re-used for operations at a later date. Robots usually have interchangeable gripping devices. Typical uses are spot welding, paint spraying, component handling and difficult assembly operations.

QUICK TEST

1. What is solid modelling?
2. Give three advantages of using CAM in industry.
3. Give two examples of industrial CAM machines.
4. State two advantages of using CAD packages.
5. What is meant by an industrial robot?
6. What useful processes do robots perform in industry?

1. A computer model of how the product will look when made.
2. Reprogrammed easily, works continuously without breaks, consistent quality levels, concurrent design.
3. Computer Numerical Control (CNC) machines (such as lathes and milling machines), and Robots.
4. Can be linked to CAD and factory-wide systems for automatic assembly and machining.
5. An industrial robot is a computer-controlled device that can be programmed to carry out many different functions.
6. Can be used in hazardous conditions, processes which are difficult to control.

COMPUTER INTERGRATED SYSTEMS

WHAT IS CIM?

CIM stands for computer-integrated manufacture.
A CIM system is one which has a large part of its production process operated and controlled by computers.

PARTS OF A CIM SYSTEM

A CIM system consists of:
computer-aided design
computer-operated machinery
computer-controlled production systems
computer-controlled material handling systems.

Examiner's Top Tip
Learn the meaning of CIM and know the advantages and disadvantages.

INSTALLING CIM SYSTEMS

CIM systems are very expensive to install. They tend to be installed in industries such as automated car production and aerospace manufacturing.
CIM systems are integrated systems where the various parts of the company and its operations are linked together by computer.
They very often have a central computer which can controlled a range of operations.

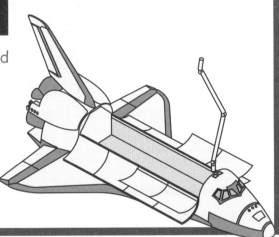

PRODUCTION CONTROL

Companies can use computers in a number of ways. These include stock control, checking maintenance requirements, monitoring where products are in the system.
Computers are used for just-in-time systems to check whether parts need ordering. The computerised system is able to re-order components and parts from supplies.

CONTROLLING EQUIPMENT

Computer-aided machinery and computer-aided drawing systems are networked to the central system. Orders can be sent to the appropriate machines and equipment. CIM systems can also have automatic handling equipment to speed up the movement of goods through the factory.

ADVANTAGES OF CIM

- Can integrate a factory so that all sections are controlled from a central point.
- Can have CAD quickly download information to computer equipment.
- Production can be monitored constantly.
- Companies can have effective links with their suppliers.
- Can produce data on many aspects of the production plant.

DISADVANTAGES OF CIM

- Expensive to install.
- Not all companies can afford it.
- Failures can cause expensive problems.
- Difficult to maintain.

QUICK TEST

1. What does CIM stand for?
2. What sort of equipment may be linked to a CIM system?
3. What sort of industries might have a CIM system?
4. What types of operational control are linked to a CIM system?
5. What are some of the disadvantages of CIM?

1. Computer-integrated manufacture.
2. Production control, maintenance, CAD, CAM.
3. Car industry, aerospace industry.
4. Just-in-time, stock control, parts control links with suppliers.
5. Expensive to install, not all companies can afford it, computers might fail, difficult to maintain.

CONTROLLING THE QUALITY

QUALITY CONTROL AND TQM

- Quality systems are important to ensure that parts and products are manufactured to the required standards and specifications.
- Inspection methods are often used to check the quality of parts either at the end of the manufacturing process or at specific points during the process.
- Quality control using purely inspection methods can lead to a large number of rejects because faults may not be found until the end of the manufacturing process.
- The total quality management (TQM) approach can improve the quality of processes and procedures and products because quality systems are introduced at every stage of production and within the organisation.
- TQM seeks to make the product right first time, every time.

QUALITY DEFINITIONS

Quality means:
- Conforming to the design specification.
- Ensuring that the product performs the task it was intended for.
- Ensuring customer satisfaction.
- Ensuring that products meet the criteria laid down in British or other standards.

Examiner's Top Tip
Know how to use templates and simple gauges to check measures for small batches of components.

VARIABLES AND ATTRIBUTES

There are two types of quality characteristics:
- Variables are characteristics which can be measured and must lie between a range of values. These include lengths, widths, heights, diameters and weights.
- Attributes are not measurable quantities but are yes/no decisions that are either acceptable or unacceptable. Examples are correct colour or missing parts.

TOLERANCE

It would be very time-consuming and almost impossible to make every product in a batch to exactly the same size.
In practice limits and tolerances are used to give the largest and smallest size permitted for a dimension:

upper limit
50.1 mm

lower limit
49.9 mm

tolerance = 50.1 - 49.9 = 0.2mm

- The upper limit is the largest dimension that is acceptable.
- The lower limit is the smallest dimension that is acceptable.
- The tolerance is obtained by subtracting the lower limit from the upper limit.

INSPECTION PROCEDURES

There are two basic types of inspection: 100% inspection and sample inspection.

100% inspection is where every product is examined.

It is often impractical to check every component during manufacture. Instead, a sample of components are checked. If an unacceptable number of rejects are found in the sample then the whole batch may be rejected and subjected to 100% inspection. Adjustments are then made to the faulty production process.

TYPES OF FIT

Tolerances are often used in conjunction with types of fit.
• A <u>clearance</u> <u>fit</u> occurs, for example, when a shaft can rotate freely in a hole. A clearance fit occurs when the shaft is smaller than the hole.

• An <u>interference</u> <u>fit</u> occurs when the shaft is larger than the hole. Interference fits are used when two parts have to be held in place, often, by the frictional forces between the two materials. Examples include location dowels in jigs and fixtures and the fit between the outside of a bearing and its housing.

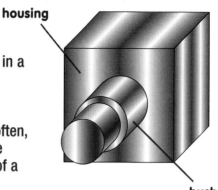

housing

bush

LIMIT GAUGES

Measuring each component in a sample using rules, callipers, micrometers and verniers would be time-consuming. In practice, gauges are used to speed up the process. A <u>gauge</u> can be used to check whether component dimensions are satisfactory or not satisfactory.

The size of a hole can be checked using a <u>plug</u> <u>gauge</u>. The GO end will enter the smallest hole the NOT GO end will not enter the largest acceptable hole.

<u>Gap</u> <u>gauges</u> are used to measure the dimensions of shafts. A shaft within limits will enter the GO end but will not enter the NOT GO end.

<u>Taper</u> <u>plug</u> <u>gauges</u> are used for checking the accuracy of tapers.

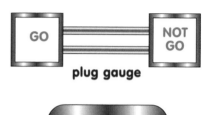

plug gauge

gap gauge

CONTROL CHARTS

• *<u>Control</u> <u>charts</u> can be used to monitor the <u>quality</u> <u>of</u> <u>a</u> <u>process</u>. Component sampling is carried out and recorded on a control chart. The chart indicates whether the products are within the <u>quality</u> <u>limits</u>. If not, the machines or processes must be stopped or adjusted.*

• *<u>ISO</u> <u>9000</u> is an internationally agreed set of <u>standards</u> <u>for</u> <u>the</u> <u>operation</u> <u>of</u> <u>quality</u> <u>management</u> <u>systems</u>. ISO 9000 specifies the procedures that manufacturers have to comply with in order to reach the quality standard. Complying with the standards indicates that a company has good quality procedures and is producing good-quality goods.*

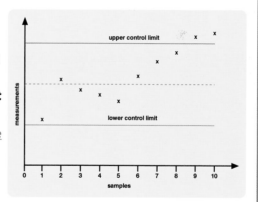

QUICK TEST

1. What is a variable?

2. What is an attribute?

3. What is meant by a tolerance?

4. Name two types of fit.

5. What is a plug gauge used to check?

6. What ISO code is an international standard?

1. A characteristic which can be measured.
2. A characteristic which can only be acceptable or unacceptable.
3. The difference between an upper and lower limit of acceptability.
4. Interference and clearance.
5. The size of holes.
6. ISO 9000.

EXAM QUESTIONS — Use the questions to test your progress. Check your answers on page 95.

1. a) What type of production is suitable for making 1,000 components of a product? (1 mark)

....

....

....

b) State two ways a jig can aid such production. (2 marks)

....

....

....

2. What is meant by the term TQM? (1 mark)

....

....

....

3. a) What does CIM mean? (1 mark)

....

....

....

b) State two ways in which CIM can be used to improve the manufacturing plant? (2 marks)

....

....

....

4. Give two advantages of using standard components in a production system. (2 marks)

....

....

....

5. Describe two quality control checks that could be carried out during manufacture. (2 marks)

....

....

....

6. State two advantages of using robots to apply spray paint finishes. (2 marks)

....

....

....

7. a) What is meant by the term JIT? (1 mark)

....

....

....

b) Give an advantage of using JIT when manufacturing. (1 mark)

....

....

....

8. State the four main categories of manufacture. (4 marks)

....

....

....

9. What type of engineering is used to reduce the time it takes from the design stage to manufacture? (1 mark)

....

....

....

10. What is meant by the term jig? (2 marks)

....

....

....

11. Give two advantages of using computer-aided machines (CAM) during manufacture. (2 marks)

....

....

....

How did you do?

0–2	correct	....start again
3–5	correct	....getting there
6–8	correct	....good work
9–11	correct	....excellent

ANSWERS

Materials and Components

1. a) Acrylic, ABS, PVC

b) Its ability to bend by heat forming, can be cut and shaped easily and it can be re-cycled easier than plastics.

2. a) Beech

b) It can be coloured, has smooth corners, can have intricate details, is durable.

3. a) Nuts, bolts, washers, set screws, rivets, dowels, bearings, gears etc (any three).

b) It is cheaper, do not have to have a manufacturing set-up for the parts, the suppliers are responsible for quality.

4. a) Materials: expanded polystyrene, bubble wrap, card, polystyrene (any two)

Reasons: materials are light weight, absorb impact and transparent

b) Are they bio-degradable? Can they be recycled? (any one)

5. a) Good corrosion resistance, good strength, good durability

b) It would corrode due to weather and soil.

c) Clean, degrease and paint with cellulose paint.

6. It uses recycled materials, does not waste parts of the wood as in the case of rough cut timber.

7. a) i) Box: oak, mahogany, beech, pine etc

ii) Handle: PVC, nylon, high-impact polystyrene

b) Box: easy to clean, durable, light

Handle: decorative, durable, good strength

c) Injection moulding

8. a) 0.7—1% carbon steel

b) To remove brittleness.

c) By colours or by using a furnace set at the correct temperature.

9. a) Glass fibre reinforced plastics

b) It is light, has good corrosion resistance, is easily moulded, can be repaired easily (any two).

c) Hand lay-up

10. a) Teak, oak

b) Protection against moisture, insects, fungi (any two).

11. a) Tensol cement

b) Needs to be clean, good finish required on edges of plastics, needs to be held firmly whilst setting.

12. a) Good corrosion resistance, light, good strength, good durability (any two).

b) Polystyrene, nylon

c) Aluminium or stainless steel

Design and Market Influences

1. Needs to support card, be attractive, be durable, make it easy to replace cards (any three)

2. a) Linear (handle)

b) Rotary (oscillating)

c) Input = turning the handle; output = movement of the wings.

d) A linkage

3. a) The size of equipment, number of equipment, where tidy is going to be kept.

b) If holes are not the same size, it may not be aesthetically pleasing, the pens might fall out.

4. a) Cam

b) It is easy to fit into toy, has a reliable mechanism.

5. a) Computer Aided Design

b) Solid modelling of the product, 2D work, design drawings, detail drawings (any two).

6. Ask the views of the consumers, test parts, evaluate against the specification.

7. Will not totally use up the plastic non-renewable resource.

8. Mass-produced for cheapness, throwaway, may be linked to fashion (any two).

9. Veneered board uses less timber, chipboard uses less felled trees, flat pack needs less storage space (any two).

10. Ensure that paint used is not toxic, that a design does not include too many small parts, the design should not use anything sharp (any two).

11. a) Wooded: traditional-looking, durable, blend in with the surroundings

b) Plastic: maintenance free, lighter to move around, easy to wipe clean

12. Ensure there are no electrical hazards or trailing wires, minimise heat from the bulb, light needs to be stable.

Hand and Machine Processes

1. Plastics fed into hopper → heated and forced through screw → heated plastics forced into split mould → mould is cooled → mould opened and the component ejected

94

2. a) mild steel or aluminium

b) It is quicker, reduces waste, good repeatable accuracy.

3. i) Cutting wood from corners ii) planing wood flat and to size iii) finishing curved surfaces.

4. a) Hole saw

b) A pilot hole guides the tool more easily and makes cutting more accurate.

5. Securely clamp work, select correct speed, machine switched off whilst changing drills, appropriate eye protection, no dangerous loose clothing (any two).

6. a) Can be assembled and taken apart quickly

b) It reduces waste, is quicker to produce, is more cost effective, repeatable accuracy.

7. Drill hole with tapping drill, use taper thread to cut first thread, finish off with a second tap.

8. a) Strip heater, line bending machine.

b) Laminating

9. a) Tenon saw

b) Hacksaw

c) Coping saw

10. By using a four-jaw chuck.

11. a) Sand casting

b) Less waste, produces an acceptable finish, pattern can be re-used, cheap method to use (any one).

12. (i) Electrical soldering (ii) welding or brazing (iii) soft soldering.

Assembly and Finishing Methods

1. Mark out angle on the steel tubes, hacksaw to the line, file joint.

2. a) PVA glue

b) Use a try square to check angles or measure across the diagonals of the frame to ensure that they are the same length.

3. a) Scriber, centre punch, dividers

b) Hacksaw and file.

4. a) Mortise and tenon joint.

b) i) Marking out: try square, rule, sharp pencil, mortise gauge

ii) producing the joint: tenon saw for cutting the tenon; mortise chisel for cutting out the mortise.

5. i) Marking lines: chinagraph pencil, felt marker.

ii) Sawing: coping saw, jig saw, hacksaw.

iii) Finishing: file, wet and dry paper, acrylic polish, emery cloth.

6. a) Locknut

b) spring washer, nut with nylon insert.

c) The joint needs to be clean, correct type of solder used, need to use a flux, joint should be heated to the correct temperature (any two).

7. a) Painting, plastic coating (any one).

b) By carefully filing up the joint and then using emery cloth to clean to good finish.

8. a) By clamping pieces of wood across the edges of the wood to be filed so that it prevents the outside of the wood from splitting.

b) i) Drilling a pilot hole. ii) Using a bradawl.

9. Draw filing using a piece of emery cloth wrapped around a file.

10. a) They are used to clamp round bars to aid marking out or drilling.

b) The surface gauge is used help accurately mark out lines on components using the surface plate datum.

Industrial Applications

1. a) Batch production

b) More accurate, more efficient, reduces costs, speeds up production (any two).

2. Total Quality Management

3. a) Computer Integrated Manufacture

b) Accuracy from using machines, integrates the various parts of the plant, can help monitor production, can be used to link design to manufacture (any two).

4. Saves time, reduces cost of manufacturing, consistent quality (any two).

5. Measuring the dimensional accuracy of parts, checking surface finishes, checking material quality, checking if the product works properly (any two).

6. They can work in hazardous conditions, can work at the same rate without getting tired, consistent spraying, can be re-programmed for different jobs (any two).

7. a) Just In Time (manufacturing)

b) Reduces stock levels, reduces waste materials, ensures that there is not large quantities of products that cannot be sold when production has finished (any one).

8. Jobbing production, batch production, in line production, continuous production.

9. Concurrent engineering.

10. A device that clamps the work and guides the tool.

11. Can be re-programmed for different jobs, consistent quality levels, can be linked to design, can speed up production, can work continuously without breaks (any two).

INDEX